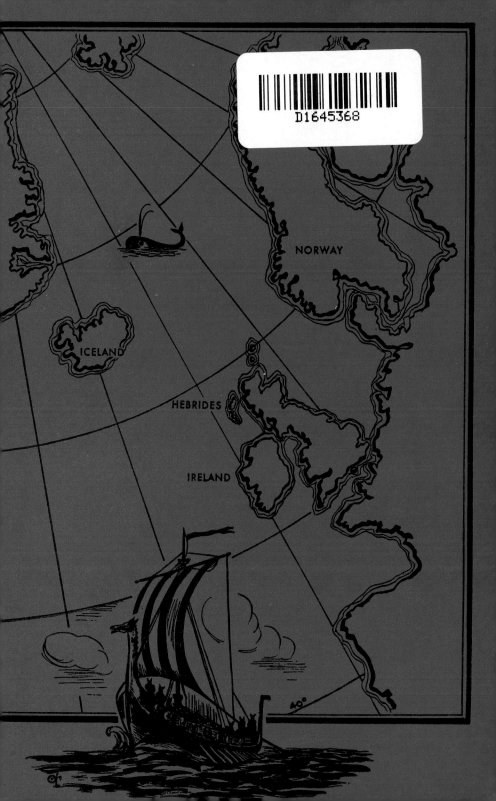

VINLAND
THE GOOD

Written by
NEVIL SHUTE

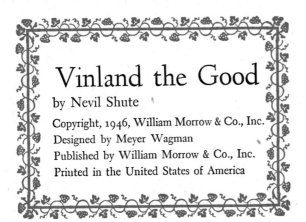

Vinland the Good

by Nevil Shute

Copyright, 1946, William Morrow & Co., Inc.
Designed by Meyer Wagman
Published by William Morrow & Co., Inc.
Printed in the United States of America

PREFACE

Some years ago I came upon the historical story of the discovery of America by Leif Ericsson in A.D. 1003. I think this is one of the most fascinating adventures in history. This was no grandiose expedition of great people setting out in pomp and dignity from all the splendour of a Spanish royal court. This was a journey by the common man, a farmer, seeking to get a load of lumber to build cowhouses and discovering America on the side. I prefer that sort of story myself.

I put a very little of it into a novel which was published in 1939. During the war years the story stayed in my mind as one of the best I knew; I told it many times in wardrooms and in messes, and many times I kicked myself for only having written a small part of it. At the end of 1944 I was demobilized, and filled in time while waiting to go out to Burma on another job by writing the whole story out in full. I did not want to write it as another novel on the same subject, so I wrote it as the treatment for a film. That is the story in this book.

All the historical characters that I have named were real people, and their actions were substantially as I have described them. I have deviated from history in one very small particular at the extreme end of the story; the student may have fun in finding out this liberty. Apart from that, the story is as true a representation of what happened as any novelist can be expected to produce.

I could not have written it without great help from Mr. Edward F. Gray, both in person and through his book LEIF ERIKSSON. I have also used THE NORSE DISCOVERERS OF AMERICA by Gay-thorne-Hardy, IN NORTHERN MISTS by Nansen, THE VIKING AGE by Du Chaillu, THE VIKINGS OF BRITAIN by D. P. Capper, and THE VOYAGES OF THE NORSEMEN TO AMERICA by Hovgaard. To all these authors I tender my thanks for much that has amused and interested me, but especially to Mr. Gray whose book constitutes the most modern research into this old story.

Nevil Shute

VINLAND
THE GOOD

(*The story opens with a scene in the masters' common room of an English public school. The* HEADMASTER *is talking to two of his senior assistant masters; they are between sixty and seventy years old. There are several other masters in the room; all are elderly because the time is immediately after the European war, and the young masters have not yet returned from service. These elderly masters should be serious types; they must not be farcical.*)

(*The room should be a high, bare room, sparsely furnished with little more than a long table and a few hard chairs. There should be a picture of the Colosseum and several group photographs of the staff in bygone years upon the walls.*)

HEADMASTER Now about this period of American History for the Lower Fifth. It won't do them much good to know about the History of the United States, but there seems to be a demand for it from the parents, and we must move with the times. I should like one of you to take that on.

FIRST ASST. MASTER Which period had you in mind?

HEADMASTER Monday, ten to eleven.

SECOND A. M. (*Quickly*) But that's when they do their Greek Testament! Surely you aren't going to give the History of the United States precedence over the Greek Testament?

HEADMASTER How stupid of me. Well, it will have to be Thursday between three and four. We could start them off to-day.

SECOND A. M. (*Ponderously*) I'm afraid it's hardly in my line. I know nothing about America, except that their police force seems to be remarkably inefficient. Keystone Police, I think they call them.

FIRST A. M. I take the Upper Fourth for grammar in that period. If we've got to teach them all this modern nonsense you'll have to find someone else. Isn't anybody joining us this term at all?

HEADMASTER Well, there's Callender—he's coming back to-day. I had a telegram. We might try him with it. After all, it isn't very important.

FIRST A. M. Young Callender, who went off to the war in 1939?

HEADMASTER That's the one.

SECOND A. M. I don't remember him. What was he like?

HEADMASTER He's in this group. (*Turns to a framed group of masters as in 1939, and points out an undeveloped, weedy young man to them.*) That's Callender.

SECOND A. M. I don't know that I think much of him. Could he keep his form in order?

HEADMASTER No.

FIRST A. M. After six years in the Army he may have learned to manage a few boys. Anyway, he's six years older now. Wasn't History one of his subjects, by the way?

HEADMASTER Now you mention it, I think it was.

SECOND A. M. Was he a good scholar?

FIRST A. M. Good enough to take this nonsense off our shoulders.

HEADMASTER He took a Second at Oxford, but he was always very eccentric. (*The others nod with understanding.*) I remember when he put the Lower Sixth to writing an account of Mae West taking tea with the Archbishop of Canterbury, in Greek Iambics. I had to speak to him quite sharply about that.

[DISSOLVE TO:

School Entrance

(MAJOR CALLENDER *is driving in to the school grounds in a very old taxi driven by a very old man. CALLENDER is a vigorous man of about twenty-seven, sunburnt, with a slightly whimsical expression. He is dressed in very new civilian clothes but his luggage is all service—bedding roll, kitbag, etc.; he carries a service waterproof with the major's crown still on the epaulette. He sits upright on the edge of the seat, looking keenly and enthusiastically at the familiar school grounds—mown lawns, tall elm trees, etc. The taxi draws up at the Headmaster's house, and CALLENDER gets out.*)

Headmaster's Study

(*This is a well-furnished, comfortable room, lined with book-cases. There is a bust of Plato, and a large picture of the Acropolis. The* HEADMASTER *is seated at his desk. A very old* BUTLER *opens the door.*)

BUTLER Major Callender is here, sir.

HEADMASTER Major . . . Oh, of course. Show him in.

(*He gets up from his desk to greet* CALLENDER, *who comes in to the room enthusiastically.*)

HEADMASTER My dear boy, it's a very great pleasure to see you here again, after all these years.

CALLENDER I'm terribly sorry to arrive so late, sir. There was some bloody muck up—(*The* HEADMASTER *winces.*)—about my demobilization, and I didn't leave Palestine till Monday, and then there was a balls about my transport. But I managed to cadge a lift in a Beaufighter that was going down to Cairo, and there I said I had despatches for the War Office—you've got to say something, you know—and I got a ride in a Dakota. We put down at Athens and Rome and got in yesterday morning. I got myself some civvy clothes and came straight here.

HEADMASTER (*Glancing at the print of the Acropolis*) Athens —Palestine. I have always wanted to pay a visit to the Holy Land.

CALLENDER (*Frankly*) I wouldn't go there if I were you—it's a stinking bloody place. Nothing but a pack of lousy Jews and Arabs slitting each other's throats. I'm damn glad to be out of it.

HEADMASTER (*Studying him thoughtfully*) Sit down, my boy, and tell me all about yourself. What have you been doing all these years? (*They light cigarettes from a silver box upon the desk.*)

12

CALLENDER Well, I was an Ack-Ack gunner in the Battle of Britain, and then they sent me to Libya. I was in Tobruk all the siege. When we got relieved they kept me there, so that I got captured with the second Tobruk party. I was in a prisoners of war camp near Pisa for fourteen months, but I walked out of that when the Italians signed their Armistice. Five weeks after that I managed to get down and join up with our party at Anzio.

HEADMASTER But do you mean that you were wandering about behind the German lines?

CALLENDER That's right. It was bloody good fun.

HEADMASTER But could you talk Italian?

CALLENDER I can now. Anyway, after that I turned over to the Parachute crowd. We dropped near Oustrehem the night before the Normandy show opened and managed to hold on until the Pongos got to us; that was a good party. Then I got in to another one that wasn't quite so hot, at Arnhem. I got taken prisoner when we had to pack up, but I got away. It's pretty easy to do that in the first few hours, you know.

HEADMASTER (*Faintly*) I suppose it is.

CALLENDER Well, after that they sent me out to Palestine, and here I am.

HEADMASTER Do you know, that's a very wonderful story of adventure.

CALLENDER Is it? I suppose it might look like that to you. It's six wasted bloody years to me. When you're in the Army you've just got to do your best with the next thing that turns up, and chance it. Thank God it's all over.

HEADMASTER Do you think that after all this roving about you'll be able to settle down to our quiet life here, and our rather humdrum affairs? They are very important to us, you know. I have

13

known the most bitter feuds arise among the staff over a minor alteration in the timetable, or the allocation of an hour to chemistry.

CALLENDER Don't worry about that. All the time that I've been roving about, as you call it, I've been thinking of this place, and wanting to get back here to the dear old school. All through, when everything has been thoroughly raw and stinking, I've thought that I'd be coming back here one day, if I didn't buy it first. It's—it's quiet here, and dignified, and serene.

HEADMASTER You felt like that about it?

CALLENDER It's meant a great deal to me, while I've been in the Army, having something like this to look forward to.

HEADMASTER I'm glad of that. You don't think that it will prove to be too gentle a life for you now?

CALLENDER No. I've been offered a lot of jobs in the last few months, but I turned them all down because I wanted to come back here.

HEADMASTER What sort of jobs?

CALLENDER Commercial things. The best of them was a chap who wanted me to start a Continental selling agency for an electric razor—absolutely cracking job, half the cost of the American ones and a better article. He offered fifteen hundred a year and commission—live in Paris. But I turned it down. I wanted to come back here.

HEADMASTER (*A little uncertainly*) Well, money isn't everything.

CALLENDER Damn right, it's not.

HEADMASTER Well now, as you know, term started yesterday. I take it that you've come prepared to start work at once?

14

CALLENDER Any time you say, sir. The sooner the better. I shall be a bit rusty on some subjects, I'm afraid, but I expect I'll get by.

HEADMASTER Well, I was thinking that we might break you in gently. History was your special subject, so far as I remember. How would you like to concentrate on teaching History for this first term? I could arrange for you to take the Upper Fourth, and the Upper and Lower Fifth, and the Remove, and the Lower Sixth —all in History. And perhaps Latin for the Third Form, the very little boys.

CALLENDER (*Gratefully*) That's awfully kind of you, sir. That would give me time to get settled down and mug up all the subjects I've forgotten.

HEADMASTER You're fairly sure about your History, are you?

CALLENDER Oh, yes. I read a lot when I was in the prison camp in Italy. I was allowed to use a library in Pisa that had some good stuff in it.

HEADMASTER Splendid. The Lower Fifth are starting on the History of the United States this term. You could start them off on that this afternoon, if you feel up to it at such short notice.

CALLENDER That's all right by me. Just general, introductory stuff, I suppose?

HEADMASTER That's it—just a general introduction to the subject for this first lesson. We can plan a detailed syllabus to-morrow.

(*Outside the school bell begins to toll, and there is the sound of shuffling boys' feet. The* HEADMASTER *and* CALLENDER *leave the study and walk through typical outdoor school scenes to the classroom block and upstairs to a classroom, passing through and mingling with the crowds of boys. All through these short scenes the bell is tolling. In the classroom the boys settle at their desks. They are about sixteen years of age, typi-*

15

cal English schoolboys, interested in the sight of a new master and resolved to make his life a burden if they can get away with it. The HEADMASTER *and* CALLENDER *mount the dais and face them; the boys become quiet, and the bell stops.*)

The Classroom

HEADMASTER Pay attention to me, please. This is Mr.—er—Major Callender, who has joined the staff this term. None of you will remember him, but he is not a stranger to the school. He was with us for a year before the war, and now he has come back to us again after six years of military duty to take up his peacetime avocations. I am sure you will all join with me in giving him a hearty welcome. And—(*a little threateningly*)—I am sure that you will do everything you can to make things easy for him.

(*There is a pause. The* BOYS *grin furtively at one another, giving the impression that they intend to do nothing of the sort.*)

—Well now, Major Callender is going to start you off this afternoon on the History of the United States. As you all know, the United States is a very great country. Not only is it big in size, but it is big in—er—big in—well, as I was saying, it's a very great country. I am sure you will all realize that it is fitting that we should know something of the history of our greatest ally. I shall leave you with Mr. Callender.

(*He goes out. There is a vacant classroom next door, and between the two rooms there is a communicating door. The* HEADMASTER *goes into the vacant room and gently opens the communicating door a crack, in order that he may listen to the lesson unobserved. He sits down at a desk.*)

CALLENDER Well now, I'm going to tell you something about the United States, our greatest ally, as the Headmaster said.

BOY ONE (*A grave, serious type*) Sir, wasn't Russia our greatest ally? The population of Russia is much larger than the United States.

(*There are grins around the form at this opening gambit.*)

CALLENDER Well—they both fought very well.

BOY ONE The Russians started fighting first, sir. *And* they're bigger.

BOY TWO Don't pay any attention to him, sir—none of the other masters do. He's all wet.

BOY THREE None of them fought as long as we did, did they, sir?

CALLENDER It's about time you learned something about the United States. They fought by making things for us in their factories and sending them to us on Lend-Lease, long before they came into the war. At that time that was what we needed most. We hadn't got enough guns and tanks and aeroplanes to arm the fighting men we had. We didn't want any more men, at that stage of the war.

BOY THREE (*Innocently*) What *is* Lend-Lease, sir?

CALLENDER Lend-Lease? Why, that was an arrangement that we made with the United States . . . (*He realizes that he has been steered onto a side track, and stops.*) Remind me to tell you about Lend-Lease on the last day of term. This afternoon I'm going to tell you about the history of the United States.

BOY FOUR (*A big, athletic type, more adult than the rest*) Please, sir, may I leave the room?

(*There are furtive smiles around the class.*)

CALLENDER You've only just come in.

17

BOY FOUR I'm not very well, sir.

CALLENDER (*Eyeing him grimly*) I'm glad to hear it.

BOY FOUR May I go, sir?

CALLENDER No.

BOY FOUR (*Very much aggrieved*) Sir, I shall have an accident.

(*There are open titters in the class.*)

CALLENDER You'll have another one if you don't shut up.

(*The* BOY *sitting next to* BOY FOUR *moves ostentatiously away from him.*)

—Now for our history of the United States. I think we'd better start at the beginning. Can anybody tell me who first discovered America?

BOY THREE (*In a bored tone*) Christopher Columbus.

CALLENDER Wrong. Anybody else got any ideas?

BOY ONE John Cabot discovered America, sir. Christopher Columbus went to the West Indies.

CALLENDER Right, up to a point. John Cabot did discover North America, but he wasn't the first. We'll come back to him presently.

BOY TWO Sir, was John Cabot a black man?

CALLENDER No, of course he wasn't. He was born in Genoa, but he lived most of his early life in Venice till he came to England.

BOY TWO (*Innocently*) Most Americans are black, aren't they?

CALLENDER Of course they're not. Only a very small percentage are black, the descendants of the freed slaves in the south.

BOY TWO Those are the better-class Americans, aren't they, sir? Better than the white ones?

CALLENDER Why, no. Whatever put that idea into your head?

BOY TWO Well, sir, we had them in the Camp, up on the Heath. There were some white Americans to start with; then they went away and the black ones came, and there were many more of them. Everybody in the village said the black ones were much nicer. They were so quiet and helpful, sir, and they never got drunk.

BOY THREE That's right, sir. They were quite black, all over. They drove trucks awfully well.

CALLENDER Well, those were the descendants of the Negro slaves. We shall get to those about half term. But now I want to know if any of you can tell me who was the first discoverer of America, the very first that we have any record of?

(*The class are not interested; there is a dead, bored silence. A* Boy *flips a wad of paper at another* Boy *across the room with a bit of elastic between two fingers;* Callender *sees this, and is annoyed.*)

CALLENDER (*Irritably*) Well, America was first discovered by a bloody fool called Bjarni, about the year one thousand and two.

(*He turns to the blackboard and writes,* bjarni a.d. 1002. *The class shows a flicker of interest.*)

BOY FOUR (*Curiously*) Sir, why was he a bloody fool?

(*In the next room, behind the door, the corners of the* Head-master's *mouth droop; he does not approve of this conversation at all.*)

CALLENDER He saw it, but he didn't land—and there were other reasons, too. I'll tell you about him in a minute. Now, does anybody know who first explored the United States—the first that we have any record of?

19

(*Dead silence.*)

—Well, it was first explored by two young Scots, about the year one thousand and three, in the summer. They were a young man and a young woman, Haki and Haekia, born at Aberdeen or Inverness on the east coast of Scotland. I rather think they went there for their honeymoon.

(*The class is now definitely interested.* CALLENDER *turns and writes upon the blackboard* HAKI *and* HAEKIA.)

BOY FOUR Did they go to Niagara Falls, sir?

CALLENDER No. As a matter of fact, they went to Cape Cod.

BOY ONE (*Doubtfully*) It says John Cabot in the book, sir.

CALLENDER Then the book's wrong. I'm telling you what happened.

(*In the next room the* HEADMASTER *is looking very sour. In the classroom* CALLENDER *leans forward on his desk; he now has the attention of the class.*)

CALLENDER It all began about twenty years before, when a chap called Eric the Red got chucked out of Norway for manslaughter. He was a berserk.

BOY TWO What's a berserk, sir?

[DISSOLVE TO:

Hillside in Norway

(*This dissolve should take place very slowly to a scene of violence in wild Norwegian country. From now onwards* CALLENDER'S *voice will be used as a commentary when required.*

This dissolve should last as long as the following speech.)

CALLENDER A berserk was a sort of gangster tough, a regular bad lot. The sort of man who kidnapped another fellow's wife and carried her away into the hills and lived with her. Then when the husband came to get her back the berserk worked himself up into a fighting rage and killed the husband in battle. This chap Eric had red hair, and he always fought in a mad fury, and he fought a lot.

(*The dissolve gradually discloses a dead man lying on the ground.* ERIC THE RED *is standing over him with a blood-stained battle axe; his anger has now cooled, and he does not know quite what to do next. He is an enormous, violent man, but in later life he made a number of loyal friends, so there must be an attractive side to him.*)

(*In the background, by a mean hovel on the hillside which may be rather like an Irish turf cottage, there is a* WOMAN *weeping.*)

(*The dissolve is now complete.* ERIC *picks up his axe and crosses uncertainly to the* WOMAN *and touches her on the shoulder.*)

WOMAN Don't touch me. I never want to see you again.

ERIC I think we will go away now, far from here, to some other place.

WOMAN I thought that would be the next thing. Go on, then. Run away and hide. You've done that before.

ERIC (*Uncomfortably*) It will make less trouble if we go away for a bit. I will take you with me.

WOMAN If you force me to come with you, I will tell the story of this murder everywhere you go.

21

ERIC It wasn't murder. He attacked me first. A man has a right to defend himself.

WOMAN There is justice in this land, and you will not escape it.

ERIC (*Irritably*) Stop snivelling, unless you want a beating.

[DISSOLVE TO:

The Thingplain

(*This was a wide, open, grassy space in front of the temple. The Thing was an assembly of the people; it was half parliament and half religious in character. It was presided over by the temple priest, the Godi, who was assisted by a council of elders known as Thingmen. The* GODI *always had a long beard.*)

(*This is an open air scene of rough, primitive people in wild scenery. They have come together to deliver justice according to their well-defined code of laws.*)

ERIC Don't keep on talking about murder. He attacked me first. I was just defending myself.

GODI But you had his woman.

ERIC A woman has the right to change her man. She stayed with me willingly, after the first day or two.

GODI That is so, but her new husband must pay compensation for the damage he has done in taking her. Did you offer to do so?

ERIC (*Loftily*) I am a man of ideals. I do not buy and sell my women.

GODI That's not a straight answer. Did you pay compensation for this woman, according to our law?

22

ERIC I am a wandering man; I have no farm and no property. I would have paid him some day, when I got some money.

(*There is a murmur in the crowd, and a surge of discontent.*)

GODI Can you pay compensation for this man that you have killed, in order that his relatives may be appeased?

ERIC (*Angrily*) Don't keep on at me. I have told you that I am a poor man; I've had a lot of bad luck recently. I will do what I can.

GODI If you cannot pay compensation, or if you will not, the relations of this man may hunt you down and kill you. They may take your life in payment for the life that you have taken. This is our ancient law.

A MAN IN THE CROWD Ay, and we'll see that the law is kept this time. We're fed up with this.

ERIC (*Fiercely, loosening the axe at his belt*) I am a man of peace. I'm not a man who goes round picking quarrels. But if any of you lawyers comes to trouble me I'll hack him in two pieces at one blow and throw the pieces to the ravens.

(*There is a hostile roar from the crowd.*)

GODI Silence, all of you. We will not have a battle raging through our country; we have had enough of that. Lawman, what is our first law?

(*The LAWMAN steps forward. This is a very old, venerable man, the most respected man in the community after the GODI. His duty was to know all the laws by heart, and to recite them on occasions such as this.*)

LAWMAN It is the first law of our man-holiness that every man of the country shall be peace-holy, both at home and abroad.

23

(There is a respectful murmur of assent from the crowd.)

GODI *(Turning to the* ELDERS) Thingmen, my advice to you is this. If we keep this man Eric in this country we shall have blood feuds according to our law, and no man will be able to work safely in his fields. I say that this man is a bad man. He will never be peace-holy. He makes continual trouble for us and he does no work; he is useless to our country. Therefore, I think that he should be an outlaw, and his father Thorvald with him, who is just as bad. I say that they should get out of this country in one week from now. If they don't go, then I think that every man should stop his work and take up arms, and hunt them down till they are killed like dogs. Thingmen, what do you say to that?

(There is a roar of assent from the crowd. The THINGMEN, *standing a little apart, consult together for a moment, and then nod their heads.)*

ERIC That's no punishment, to leave a pettifogging place like this. You're so tied up with conventions and restrictions here that a man can't breathe. I shall go westwards, over the seas to the great open spaces where men are men and not little creeping rats.

(There is an angry murmur from the crowd.)

—I shall go to Iceland, and to hell with all the lot of you.

(He turns, spits on the ground, and stalks out of the Thing- plain with some dignity.)

[DISSOLVE TO:

The Classroom

(CALLENDER *turns to a map of the North Atlantic on the wall and indicates on it with a billiard cue.)*

CALLENDER   This is Norway, where they started from, and they were going to Iceland, here. They had no compass to steer by; the magnetic compass came from China later on. But they could find their way about the seas all right. What they did was this—

[DISSOLVE TO:

The Ship

(*The scene is in the ship, where the action is in accordance with* CALLENDER's *commentary; the* CAPTAIN *of the ship is measuring the length of the shadow on the thwart, very serious and intent.*)

CALLENDER   They navigated by an observation of the sun at noon. Each day at noon they laid the ship at right angles to the sun and marked the length of the shadow of the bulwark on a thwart; that gave them a rough measure of the latitude. They carved notches on the thwart for the latitude of places they knew. This ship had a notch already carved for the latitude of northern Iceland, so they—

[DISSOLVE TO:

The Classroom

(CALLENDER *is indicating the track of the ship on the map.*)

CALLENDER   —sailed north at first until they got to the latitude of northern Iceland, and then they sailed westwards along it till they got there—here. I'm telling you all this because it's important to the story later on. You see, a ship could only sail accurately to a place that she had been to before, where they had cut the notch upon the thwart.

25

[DISSOLVE TO:

The Bow of the Ship

(*Showing a close-up view of the dragon figurehead.*)

CALLENDER The common people thought it was because the dragon on the ship would know the way back to a place he had been to before. They were very superstitious.

[FADE TO:

A Hillside in North Iceland

(*From this hillside, one looks down onto a plain; there are two rough farms upon this plain, clearly divided by a stone wall. There is a hill stream running down and through one farm; the other has no water.*)

(ERIC *and two of his thralls are standing by this stream with spades, picks, and wooden crowbars.*)

ERIC This is the place I mean. The Gods do not make rain so that Eyiolf and Hrafn can have the lot of it, and we none at all. Odin was not thinking when he made the course of this stream.

THRALL ONE Lord, you were in Norway when Odin made this stream. No one lived upon your land because it had no water.

ERIC All land has a right to water. (*Threateningly*) That's true, isn't it?

THRALL ONE (*Quickly*) Yes, Lord.

ERIC Very well, then—get your spade and start digging. If you dig a channel through this spur here, first, the stream will go our

26

way when it is dammed. Then we will make this little landslide, here; if we prize out this stone, the earth will fall. Then we shall have water on our land, as Odin meant us to have it.

[DISSOLVE TO:

The Hillside—Later

(*The* THRALLS *have done a lot of digging, and a new channel is now clear for the stream.* ERIC *and the* THRALLS *are working with wooden crowbars to loosen a great stone; presently it falls and dams the stream.* ERIC *is very pleased, and goes down onto his land to direct the new flow of water.*)

[CUT TO:

Eyiolf's Farm

(*This is a very rude hovel, stone walls and thatch; there is a similar barn near by. A* WOMAN *comes out of the door of the farmhouse and looks at the stream which runs by; it has gone dry. There should be fish flapping about in a shallow pool to indicate the suddenness of the occurrence. The* WOMAN *runs to the barn and calls the* TWO MEN.)

WOMAN All the water has gone!

(*The* MEN *stare at the stream, and then up to the hillside where the* THRALLS *are still working. They turn and grab weapons, and start running up the hill.*)

(ERIC, *working with the water on his own farm, hears the sounds of battle; he looks up to the hillside and sees the* TWO

27

MEN *fighting with his unarmed* THRALLS; *as he watches one of them falls to the ground.* ERIC *is wearing his axe; he pulls it from his belt and starts running to the scene of the fight.*)

[CUT TO:

The Hillside

(ERIC *comes up in a mad fury; both his men are dead or dying. He rushes in in a fighting rage and kills one of the attackers with a single blow of his axe. The other flees across country;* ERIC *rushes after him and kills him as he runs, after a wild chase. This is a scene of mad violence and fury.*)

[DISSOLVE TO:

Thingplain in North Iceland

(*This scene is generally similar to the Thing scene in Norway, though the detail should be sufficiently different.*)

ERIC These men attacked my thralls and killed them both. It is the law that a man should protect his own thralls. That's all I did.

GODI It is the law that a man should be peace-holy. What is this story that I hear about the stream?

ERIC There was no water on my land except what falls in rain or snow. A man has a right to fresh water, even in a lousy place like this.

GODI Did you take their water?

ERIC It wasn't their water—it was everybody's water. They had had it for a long time. It was my turn.

28

GODI You set your thralls to take the water from their land and turn it into yours. Then Eyiolf and Hrafn slew your thralls. Then you slew them. Is that right?

ERIC You Godis are all the same; you twist things about so that they look bad for a stranger. You wouldn't dare to frame an Icelander like this; you just pick on me because I come from Norway. What sort of people do you think these were? Why did everybody call Eyiolf, Eyiolf the Foul? Why did they call Hrafn, Duelling-Hrafn? Answer that, if you can.

GODI I am not here to answer questions. I tell people what I think. It is for the Thingmen to say what they want done with you. Whether these men were good or bad, you had no right to take their water or to kill them in your fury. You came to us from Norway as an outlaw and a murderer; we gave you land and a woman for your wife. We now know that you are a man who likes a fight for a fight's sake. I think that if you stay here you will kill other men in your wild quarrels, and we shall have blood feuds and murder in our midst, and no man will be safe. (*Turning to the* THINGMEN) I say to you Thingmen that I think this man should be an outlaw to our country. I say that he should get out of our land, and take his wife and child with him. If anybody speaks for this man Eric, let him speak up now.

(*There is a murmur of assent from the crowd, but nobody speaks. The* THINGMEN *nod their heads.*)

ERIC I was a fool ever to come to a sanctimonious, hypocritical place like this. They told me in Norway that North Iceland was a stinking hole; I was a fool not to believe them. One can't even breathe here without being had up before the Thing. I shall go down south of the mountain ranges to the great open spaces where a man can live like a man. I shall go down to South Iceland, and to hell with all the lot of you.

(He turns, spits on the ground, and stalks out of the Thing-plain, followed by his wife with a baby in her arms.)

[FADE TO:

Thorgest's Farm

(HISTORICAL NOTE. The next incident in the historical story concerns the theft of dais boards. It is not clear what these were, and the design of small farmhouses, very important to this film, is far from clear. I suggest that the typical Norse farm had one large room with a low dais at one end, similar to the sleeping bench in an Eskimo house. In a large farm there would be a loft and one or two side rooms used as stores. The walls were a mixture of turf and stone five or six feet thick for warmth in winter as well as for stability: the roof was usually of timber covered with turf. Internal wood furniture and fittings were richly carved, because these people had nothing else to do in the long nights of winter. Therefore, the dais boards could reasonably be beautifully carved wooden side boards, or draught screens, to the sleeping bench. These halls must have been very draughty, since to get in any daylight for fine work it would be necessary to remove the skin membrane from the window—they had no glass.)

(The sequence opens with an external scene on the farm; it is a few years after the last outlawry. ERIC is walking up to the farm; he is in a good temper, and walks hand-in-hand with his little son LEIF, about five years old. ERIC, as usual, wears his axe. LEIF is dressed exactly like his father, and wears a miniature axe. THORGEST comes out of the farmhouse to meet them.)

ERIC *(Affably)* Good health to everybody here.

THORGEST Good health to you and yours. Are you all well?

ERIC All but me. Some lunatic left the window out last night and I had a draught all down my back. I woke up with a stiff neck. I've got it still. It's very bad.

THORGEST I'm sorry about that.

ERIC I thought I'd just step over and pick up the dais boards I lent you. One wants to make the dais cozy in the winter, or this sort of thing is bound to happen. I don't want another stiff neck.

THORGEST The dais boards?

ERIC The draught screens I lent you the autumn before last, when your wife was ill.

THORGEST Oh—those boards. I had half forgotten they were yours. My sons did a lot of work on them last winter.

(*They go into the house together, and inspect the boards, which are set up at the sides of the sleeping bench to make a low draught screen; the beds should be in place to make the purpose of the boards apparent. They may be of oak, and they should be richly carved in the manner of church screens, the carving very well done.*)

ERIC Your sons do a beautiful job of carving, Thorgest—better than anybody in this country. My wife will be very pleased with these. (*He begins to remove them;* THORGEST *stops him.*)

THORGEST Wait a minute, Eric. My sons carved these boards for *my* wife. It is true that the wood is yours, but it was quite plain when you lent it me. I'll never hear the last of it if I give you these. I'll give you others for them, plain boards, just as good.

ERIC I don't want any other boards. These ones are mine.

THORGEST The carving isn't yours.

31

ERIC I didn't ask your sons to carve them.

(*One of* THORGEST's *sons comes running into the house, agitated.*)

SON Father, the bull is out! He got past me while I was cleaning out the stall. He's out upon the cliff, where Ivar has his cows. I couldn't help it, Father—really.

(FATHER *and* SON *run out of the house, and* ERIC *and* LEIF *are left alone.* ERIC *goes to the door and watches for a moment; then he goes to the dais and removes the boards, and hurries off with them across the fields. Little* LEIF *has to run to keep up with him.*)

$$\Big[\text{ DISSOLVE TO:}$$

Eric's Farm—Exterior

(ERIC *is showing the boards to his wife,* THORHILD. LEIF *is present, and there is another smaller child grubbing about on the ground;* THORHILD *has a baby in her arms.*)

THORHILD Eric, they really are beautiful. They must have spent months carving them.

ERIC They spent all winter on it. He didn't want to let me have them at first, but he saw it my way in the end. After all, they are our boards.

THORHILD I think it was very clever of you to persuade him to let you have them back.

(*Over the hill four or five men come running furiously towards the farm; they are armed.* LEIF *plucks his father's arm to call attention to them.* ERIC *turns, sees them, and grunts in a*

resigned manner. He calls his THRALLS *from the barn;* THOR-
HILD *hurries the children indoors.*)

(THORGEST *comes up with his* Two Sons *and* THREE THRALLS;
all are armed. ERIC *meets them at the head of* FOUR THRALLS,
similarly armed.)

THORGEST (*Furiously*) You've got my dais boards! You stole
them when I was out of the house!

ERIC (*Loftily*) What's all this nonsense? You said yourself that
the boards were mine.

THORGEST You stole them when my back was turned!

ERIC You boys, your father's drunk. You'd better take him away
and put him to bed.

SON We'll show you if he's drunk. Are you going to give up
those boards?

ERIC (*Whipping the axe out of his belt*) I've had enough of
you. Get off my land now, all the lot of you, before I do you a
mischief.

SON I spent all winter on those boards, but not so that a dirty
thief like you might take them, and then bully his way out of it.

(*He rushes at* ERIC *with a drawn sword.* ERIC *steps back and
stops him with a powerful upwards swing of his axe. The* SON
falls to the ground, mortally wounded, and ALL *join in battle.
This is a violent, bloody scene.* ERIC *wades through them,
fighting with his axe in a mad fury; man after man goes down
before him.* THORGEST *runs for his life, with* ONE THRALL. *His
Two* SONS *and* Two THRALLS *are left lying dead upon the
field.*)

[DISSOLVE TO:

Thingplain in South Iceland

(This scene is generally similar to the previous Things, with changes in the detail of the setting to indicate another locality. The assembled people are divided into two groups, the smaller of which stands compactly behind ERIC. *His wife is present, with the three children.)*

GODI This was a quarrel which would have been settled peaceably by a peace-holy man. Instead of that you have killed the two sons of Thorgest and two thralls. Our country is divided, because some support you and some support Thorgest. There are two armies in our land, so that we live at war between ourselves and not at peace.

ERIC I can't help it if people side with me.

GODI It is for the Thingmen to decide what is to be done, so that we may have peace in our country. Thingmen, is it your will that I should tell you what I think?

(The THINGMEN *signify assent.)*

GODI I think this. I think that this man makes trouble wherever he goes, wherever he lives. He lived at Jaederen in Norway, and was outlawed for manslaughter. He lived at Haukadal in the north, and he was banished from there for killing men in a quarrel over a stream. Now he has killed men here, in a quarrel about dais boards. I think that if he stays in our country he will kill more men, and we shall have no peace ever again. I say that we should declare him an outlaw, and that he should get away from here in one month from now, with all his people. Thingmen, that is my advice. What do you say?

A THINGMAN If we kick him out, where can he go to? He seems to have used up most of the places.

34

ERIC (*Loftily*) Don't worry your head over that, little man. There are other worlds beyond the limits of the pigsty, though the pig may not know much about them.

(*There are angry murmurs from the crowd.*)

—You'll be doing me no harm. There is no place in this country for a man who is a man with red blood in his veins, and not a little crawling dog licking the Godi's boots.

(*More angry murmurs.*)

—There is a new land over to the west, the land that Gunnbiorn saw, the son of Ulf the Crow. A new land, where a man can spread himself.

THINGMAN You're welcome to that. It's all ice and snow and glaciers. Gunnbiorn said so.

GODI Thingmen, the decision rests with you. If anybody speaks in favour of this man, let him speak up now.

STYR (*Stepping forward. He is the spokesman for the little group standing behind* ERIC.) Well, I'm for Eric, and so is Heriulf here, and Eyiolf of Sviney, and the two Thorbrandssons; I speak for all of them, and for their people. We aren't satisfied with this at all. We like Eric, and we think that in this quarrel he was right. The dais boards were his, and a man can claim his own stuff; you're just picking on him because he's been in trouble before.

(*There is a murmur of assent from the small group behind him.*)

—If Eric goes to look for the new land that Gunnbiorn saw, I'm going with him, with my people; so will we all. There are too many people in this country anyway; there isn't enough decent land to go round, so that most of us are hungry half the time.

THINGMAN That's nothing to do with this Thing. The man

35

has killed four men in a quarrel which a reasonable person would have settled peaceably, and he will do it again if he stays here. We say that he should be outlawed in one month from now.

ERIC That's all right with me. Only a fool would want to stay in a poor land like this, where a man can't even get his rights. (*Turning to his friends*) Let me go first this year, alone with my own people to the Gunnbiorn-land. If we survive the winter in the place of rocks and glaciers, and if so many can exist in such a place, I will come back for you next year, and we'll make a new colony far from this stinking hole.

(*He turns and spits upon the plain, and stalks away, his family following behind him. Little* LEIF, *following behind his father, turns and spits in exactly the same way.*)

[DISSOLVE TO:

The Harbour

(*This is a scene in a small, rocky cove with a sandy beach.* ERIC *is setting off in a small ship of the same general design as the previous one; he is going to the new land, which was subsequently known as Greenland. His friends are all there to see him off. The ship is heavily laden with all his farm goods; there are cattle and sheep and pigs and poultry on board, and ploughs and farm implements, and a farm sledge or two, and a stack of hay, and a pile of manure, and carved household furniture, and piles of bedding and pots and pans, all in a glorious mixture. His wife and children are on board; the ship is manned by his* THRALLS *and a few other men. One very ugly, small man,* TYRKER, *should be noticed. There are perhaps fifteen persons in the ship all told.*)

ERIC (*To his friends*) Well, boys, good health to all the lot of

36

you, and thanks for all you've done to help me. Look for me next summer; if it's anything like reasonable over there, I'll be back to tell you all about it.

HERIULF   Good luck, you old redheaded rascal. If you don't turn up next year, I'll come and look for you; I'm fed up with this place. Tell me, when you reach the Gunnbiorn-land, which way will you turn, north or south?

ERIC   I shall go south. In the south a little land goes further. Tyrker here comes from a place far south of Norway; he says they get two crops in the same year there, off the same land.

STYR   It's a good story, but I bet it's a lie.

TYRKER   Lord, it is quite true.

ERIC   (*Laughing*) I'll come back and tell you if it's true or not next year. Good health to all of you.

(*He goes on board the ship, which pushes off from the land and makes towards the open sea.*)

EYIOLF   There goes the best chap in this country. I hope he gets away with it.

HERIULF   I shall join him if it's possible at all. I'm quite serious about that. It may be a hard life over there, but there'd be never a dull moment in a place with Eric.

STYR   (*Laughing*) He'll get away with it all right.

$$\Big[\text{DISSOLVE TO:}$$

The Ship

(*The ship is sailing forward over a rough sea, littered with small ice. It is a misty, rainy scene.* ERIC *stands at the steering oar at the stern, peering anxiously ahead; TYRKER is beside him. In the body of the ship THORHILD is cooking a meal over a fire made upon the rough stone slabs which are the ballast. One or two of the men are sleeping in their leather sleeping bags. An iceberg passes slowly by, half seen in the murk.)*

[FADE TO:

The Classroom

(CALLENDER is indicating on the map. The attention of the class is utterly fixed; they sit intent upon him.)

CALLENDER They sailed due west along the latitude of southern Iceland, taking an observation by the mark upon their thwart whenever the sun shone. They hit the coast of Greenland somewhere south of Angmagsalik—here. It's a rocky, desolate country, that, with no sort of vegetation—hopeless for farming.

[CUT TO:

The Ship

(They are sailing down the coast of Greenland, southwards, in fine weather. The barren nature of the coast should be shown, with the glaciers running down from the icecap. There is floating ice in the sea.)

[CUT TO:

The Classroom

CALLENDER So they sailed on down the coast, hoping to find

38

a warmer and a better country further to the south. And presently they came to the end of the land, Cape Farewell, here, and rounded it, and came to the south-west corner of Greenland—here.

[DISSOLVE TO:

The Next Room

(*The* HEADMASTER *is looking exceedingly dissatisfied.*)

HEADMASTER   All this is very interesting, but it's nothing to do with the History of the United States.

[DISSOLVE TO:

South-west Greenland

(*The ship is sailing into a wide fiord; there are mountains in the far distance at the head of the fiord. The land on each side of the fiord is fairly flat moorland, bleak and desolate, and without trees.* CALLENDER'S *voice continues as a commentary.*)

CALLENDER   It was possible farming country, this—not good, but as good as some that they had left in Iceland. It was possible for them to settle here and live; cattle could graze here in the summer, and they could raise crops. Eric settled here at a place that they called Brattahlid in Ericsfiord. They built stone houses in this place, roofing them over with driftwood; wood was very scarce, because there were no trees. Their houses are still there to-day, after nearly a thousand years.

[DISSOLVE TO:

Brattahlid To-day

(The ruins of the stone houses are seen, with a motor truck, or a motor boat, or any present-day appliance of that sort to make the contrast.)

CALLENDER They settled there, and started farming in that barren land.

[DISSOLVE TO:

Eric's Farm at Brattahlid

(General scenes of the countryside and the farm and settlement as it was in Norse times, during the following commentary by CALLENDER.*)*

CALLENDER A couple of years later, Eric sailed back to Iceland to tell his friends that he had found a land where they could farm. A number of them returned with him to Greenland as colonists. So time slipped by till fifteen years had passed, and the Greenland colony was about two hundred people strong. Remember, it was still an outlaw colony. In the year one thousand and one Eric, who was getting to be an old man, sent his eldest son Leif to Norway on a diplomatic mission.

[DISSOLVE TO:

Eric's Farm

(This is an exterior farmyard scene. ERIC, *who is now shown as a much older man, is leaning over a rail in earnest conversation with his son* LEIF.*)*

(LEIF ERICSSON *should be shown as a young man of twenty or so. He should be a strong, competent, and intelligent man.*)

ERIC We have plenty of stuff to trade with them; tell them there will be quite sufficient to make up a shipload once a year. You must take samples with you of our tusks and hides and wool, and our rare furs; they pay a lot for furs at home. On our part we want iron—iron and wood. Get some of the iron in nails if you can, and some in sheets—I'm fed up with these bone ploughs. Get about half of it in bars. Pig iron would be better than nothing; we can always work it up. Get some brass if they will let you have it.

LEIF How long should the timber be?

ERIC It is more expensive if it is long. Twenty feet will do for anything that we want here. Oak knees for shipbuilding, straight oak for ships' keels, beech for table-tops, deal planks—get about half of it in deal planks. Straight oak, if you can get it, for roof-trees and rafters.

LEIF Trust me, Father. I know what we want.

ERIC (*Thoughtfully*) I think I shall send old Tyrker with you. He's been in Norway, and he knows the ways of the King's court. It's not like this place, you know, where we are all friends. In Norway and in Iceland too, for that matter, you've got to watch your step—say Sir to this man, and Lord to another. And those Godis! I was always getting into trouble.

LEIF I expect I shall, too.

ERIC You mustn't get into trouble. We depend on you. If you don't come back next year with wood and iron goods, we'll be in a bad way. We've got to get some manufactured stuff out here, somehow. Just think about that, lad, when trouble comes your way. Think of the rest of us, waiting on what you can achieve in Norway.

41

LEIF I'll remember that, Father. I'm glad you're going to let me take old Tyrker.

[DISSOLVE TO:

The Ship

(*This may be the same ship that* ERIC *came to Greenland in. It is setting out from the fiord at Brattahlid, loaded with a few bales of fur and hides. There are about fifteen or twenty men on board.* LEIF *is at the steering oar. Beside him is the small, ugly man* TYRKER, *now older than when we saw him before. The camera dwells on him.* CALLENDER'S *voice is heard in commentary.*)

CALLENDER This man Tyrker was a German, who had somehow wandered out to Greenland with the Vikings. He had been a slave but he was now a free man; the Norsemen usually made their slaves free in middle age, as a reward for good service. This Tyrker had stayed on with Eric as a paid servant; he was shrewd and experienced, and he had helped to bring up Leif. He was a trusted old family retainer, and as ugly as sin.

[DISSOLVE TO:

The Classroom

CALLENDER (CALLENDER *is indicating on the map*) So they sailed eastwards round Cape Farewell and then northwards up the coast of Greenland till they found the latitude of Iceland by the mark upon the thwart, and then along till they reached Iceland. They stopped there for stores and fresh water, and they got rather a chilly reception.

[DISSOLVE TO:

A Beach in Iceland

(*The ship is beached upon the sand, and* LEIF *and his party are talking to a group of hostile, elderly men. These are* THING-MEN.)

A THINGMAN   I know you. I remember you when you were a little boy, when your father was outlawed at the Thing.

ANOTHER   Is this the boy who spat?

THINGMAN   This is the one. You are an outlaw to this country still. You may buy food and take water for your ship, and then you'd better get away. We will suspend your outlawry for twenty-four hours while you do that. After that time, you must go. We don't want people like you or your father in this country.

LEIF   Twenty-four hours is plenty. Nobody in his senses would want to stay longer in a cold, desolate place like this, with cold, desolate people. I come from a far better land than this one. I wouldn't stay here if I was paid to.

THINGMAN   (*Scornfully*) A far better land! Gunnbiorn told us about it, years ago. He said it was all ice and rocks and glaciers.

LEIF   That's all you know. Gunnbiorn didn't go down to the south of it. Where we live, it's a fair, sunny, smiling land, with rich fields and warm winters. We hardly ever see snow there, and there is no ice in the sea.

(*Beside him,* TYRKER'S *mouth twitches with concealed laughter.*)

—It is a beautiful and gracious country. Our first crop ripens in March from the autumn sowing, and we get another in September off the same bit of land. One of our cows gave five hundred gallons of milk last year. We leave them out all through the winter, grazing.

A THINGMAN (*Incredulously*) How far southwards is this land?

LEIF Five days' sailing from the latitude of this place, on the coast you come to first.

A THINGMAN What is the name of this country where you live?

LEIF We call it Greenland because it is so beautiful, and because the pastures are green all the year round.

[DISSOLVE TO:

The Ship at Sea

(LEIF *is at the steering oar, with* TYRKER *by his side.* TYRKER *is laughing quietly.*)

LEIF What are you laughing at?

TYRKER I was thinking of the yarn you told those elders back in Iceland. Green pastures all the year round! Crops in March! and the cow! (*Laughs*) And the cream of the joke is, they believed every word of it!

LEIF (*Seriously*) Well, that's what Father told me to say. He said we wanted more people in our country, so that we'd produce more ivory and furs to fill the ship each year. If we couldn't fill the ship, he said, they wouldn't send it and we'd get no manufactured stuff at all.

TYRKER You'll get all Iceland if you go on talking like that.

[DISSOLVE TO:

A Hall in Iceland

(*The* THINGMEN *are in conference at a table.*)

A THINGMAN There may be some truth in it, you know. Five days' sailing to the southwards is a good distance; you can go a long way in five days with a fair wind. I wouldn't say that it's impossible, by any means.

ANOTHER We never get two crops from the same land, here in Iceland. I know such things do happen in more southerly countries. I agree—this thing wants looking into.

ANOTHER (*Doubtfully*) I never heard of any cow giving milk like that.

FIRST THINGMAN It does happen, if the pasture is good enough. We get over a gallon a day here, in the summer months. What I don't like about this story is that it all checks up so well. If these outlaws really have found a good land down to the south, we ought to take it in as part of our domain.

ANOTHER What about the outlaws? What should we do with them?

FIRST THINGMAN They could go somewhere else.

A VERY OLD MAN I think we ought to send a ship there to see what the place is really like, and come back to report to us.

A THINGMAN That's a good idea. Bjarni would be the man to send.

ANOTHER Why Bjarni? He's awfully dumb.

THINGMAN His father, Heriulf, went with Eric; Bjarni's always talking about going out to see his father.

ANOTHER Do you think he's got enough sense for a job like this? We want a decent report.

THINGMAN He's a very good seaman, and that's the main thing. He hasn't got to do anything but come back here and tell us what he saw in their green land. We can ask his crew, too.

ANOTHER Shall I go and find him?

[CUT TO:

The Same Hall in Iceland—Later

(BJARNI *is seated at the table in conference with the elders. He is a middle-aged man with a clean-shaven face like a naval officer, with a bold chin. He is pleasant, but stupid; he speaks slowly and has difficulty in expressing himself.*)

BJARNI It's a bit late in the summer for going westwards. You ought to go that way in the spring.

A THINGMAN Why is that?

BJARNI Well, everybody goes west in the spring. It's not so easy later on in the summer, you see.

THINGMAN But why? What makes it difficult to go westwards in the summer?

BJARNI (*Helplessly*) Well, I mean—the ship won't go.

THINGMAN (*Patiently*) But there's plenty of wind.

BJARNI It makes the rowing so difficult, you see. And it's a very long way.

ANOTHER THINGMAN Do you mean that you don't get a fair wind in the late summer?

BJARNI That's right. That's just what I've been saying, but I never can make landsmen understand about the sea.

46

THINGMAN That's quite right. We always get westerly winds from June onwards. I should have thought of that. It's in the spring we get the easterlies.

BJARNI That's just what I said.

THINGMAN But, Bjarni, could you get to this place, do you think? I mean, this summer.

BJARNI Oh, we'd get there all right. We'd get there somehow or other, but it might take some time. We might not be able to come back this year.

[DISSOLVE TO:

Bjarni's Ship

(*The ship is seen labouring in a rough sea, doing her best to beat against the wind on the starboard tack.* BJARNI *is working at the steering oar; he is virile and competent, and showing at his best.* CALLENDER's *voice is heard as commentary.*)

CALLENDER Well, Bjarni was quite right. He met head winds which prevented him from sailing to Greenland along his latitude, as Eric had done years before. These ships would not beat against the wind, and if the wind was strong you could not row them up against the wind, either. Bjarni had to bear away southwards and work to the west as best he could each day, as the wind veered and changed. He was hindered by the fact that he had no compass and he didn't know the latitude of the place that he was going to; his ship had never been there before, so he hadn't got the notch upon his thwart. He didn't know where he was going to or how far he had gone towards it, but he went on. He was a very brave man.

47

[DISSOLVE TO:

The Classroom

(CALLENDER *is indicating on the map.*)

CALLENDER He came down here, zigzagging about in his head winds, trying to get westwards. He ended up by missing Greenland altogether; he passed south of Cape Farewell, here. By that time he had been a long time at sea and he didn't in the least know where he was, but he went on. He was that kind of man. And in the end, he came out on the coast of Newfoundland, here. And he was very disappointed.

[DISSOLVE TO:

Bjarni's Ship

(*The ship is shown sailing near the coast of a well-wooded, fertile country in fine, sunny weather. This should be a very beautiful scene, in contrast to the rough seas and grey skies of the previous shots. The crew are all staring at the shore, entranced.* BJARNI *is at the helm, and looking very discontented.*)

FIRST MAN Lord, it's been worth a bad passage to come out at a fine country like this one. It's the best country I have ever seen.

BJARNI We have come wrong, all thanks to those infernal head winds. This is not the place that we are looking for.

FIRST MAN Are you sure of that, Lord? Leif Ericsson said that there was pasture, and there is pasture here, and fine weather, and tall trees.

48

BJARNI I know what I am doing. They told me definitely that I should come to a bad land of rocks and glaciers first; this place is nothing like it. We have come wrong.

SECOND MAN But, Lord, this is a good land.

BJARNI It's not the land that we are looking for. We will sail north for a bit, and see if we can find the bad land with the rocks and glaciers. From there we have to sail south for five days and turn the corner of the land, and we shall come to Ericsfiord.

FIRST MAN Lord, we haven't got much water left, and there is very little wood. Shall we go in to the beach and land in this good place, and find a stream, and cut some wood? We have been a long time at sea.

BJARNI Nonsense. We've got plenty of wood, and there are two whole barrels of water that we haven't touched yet. Of course we won't land; we are going on to find the place with the rocks and the glaciers. You just want a run on shore, that's all that's the matter with you. I often wonder why chaps like you go to sea at all, if you don't like it.

FIRST MAN I often wonder that myself.

BJARNI Get forward, and slack off the weather sheet. (*Hails*) Stand by the vangs; heave in on the lee sheet. Leadsman, what water have you got?

$$\left[\text{FADE TO:} \right.$$

Bjarni's Ship—Later

(*The ship is seen off the coast of Labrador, sailing northwards. The coast is misty and rocky.* BJARNI *is looking puzzled and discontented.* CALLENDER'S *voice is heard as commentary.*)

CALLENDER He sailed north up the coast of Newfoundland and the country got worse, of course, as he went northwards. He came to Labrador and it was worse still, but there were no glaciers to set his mind at rest. And after a few days of this he was completely foxed. He had no interest in the land he had discovered, and he could find nothing in the least like Greenland. The season was getting late, so he thought he'd better get back to Iceland.

[DISSOLVE TO:

The Classroom

CALLENDER Well, that seemed easy enough. He had a fair southwesterly wind, and he knew the latitude of Iceland because he had the notch for Iceland carved upon his thwart. So he set out upon a northeast course, like this, meaning to come to the latitude of Iceland well to the west, and sail along till he got home. He turned his back upon America.

[CUT TO:

Bjarni's Ship

(*The ship is seen standing out eastwards, away from the land.*)

[CUT TO:

The Classroom

CALLENDER And so, following on that course, he hit the southwest corner of Greenland, here, and came to Ericsfiord—more by luck than good management.

50

[DISSOLVE TO:

Bjarni's Ship

(*The ship is seen beaching at Brattahlid. All the colony are on the beach to greet the travellers, headed by* ERIC.)

[DISSOLVE TO:

The Classroom

CALLENDER The season was too far advanced for them to risk the journey back to Iceland that year, and so they stayed for the winter; Bjarni stayed with his father, Heriulf. In the meantime, Leif had gone on his way from Iceland, and he, too, had trouble with the weather. He went like this (*indicates on the map*) and he put in at the Hebrides, here, to wait for a fair wind. He found he wasn't very welcome.

[FADE TO:

A Harbour in the Hebrides

(LEIF'S *ship is coming into a small made harbour, with a stone quay and a few rude houses behind it. The King of the Islands is standing on the quay, fully armed; there are a number of armed men behind him. The* KING *should be a hard, ruthless, Puritan type. One or two powerful Viking warships are in the harbour, in contrast to* LEIF'S *merchant ship, which is small and old. In this sequence the impression must be held throughout that* LEIF'S *party are greatly outnumbered.*)

51

(The ship comes to the quay. It is evident that they have had a long, hard passage. There is water in the ship, and the men are exhausted and wet. There should be slight damage; a broken steering oar, tears patched in the sail, etc.)

KING Who are you people? What do you want here?

LEIF We are on our way to King Olaf in Norway, but the winds are foul and we can't lie anywhere near our course. We are a long time out from Iceland. My name is Leif, the son of Eric the Red. We come from a country over to the west of Iceland, that we call Greenland. May we stay here till the wind is fair for Norway?

KING You are Leif Ericsson?

LEIF I am.

KING I have heard of your father. You are outlaws both from Norway and from Iceland.

LEIF That's true of my father, though we think that he was badly used. For myself—I am technically an outlaw in Iceland, though I was only six years old when we left. I am a free man in Norway. That is why my father sent me on this mission to the King instead of going himself, so that I might speak for him and for our people as a free man.

KING I'll have no outlaw in my country, even whitewashed ones.

LEIF Surely, sir, whatever you may think of us, you won't refuse us shelter here till the wind changes? We've been a long time at sea, and we intend to make no trouble.

(The KING turns aside and speaks in conference with one or two of his men. This is a moment of tension in the boat.)

KING *(Turning back to LEIF)* I will not refuse a refuge to seafarers, if they behave themselves. Beyond that point, there, you will find a little bay, and a green sward of grass. You may land there, and camp. You may not stray beyond the grassy patch without my leave; you may not talk to any of my people. You can stay there till the wind changes, and no longer. God help you if you make any trouble in this country.

[DISSOLVE TO:

Leif's Camp

(*The ship is beached in a little bay. The Norsemen have made a camp on shore, very near their ship. They have put up two tents, a large one for the men and a small one for* LEIF; *these tents are of leather well made and efficient. There is a small fire in a stone hearth before* LEIF's *tent—an important feature later on. There is another very large fire near the men's tent. They are drying all their bedding, spare clothes, sleeping bags, etc., before this fire, so that the camp is in a great confusion of drying clothes and steam.*)

(*A* GIRL *walks over the hill down to the camp by the ship. This is* THORGUNNA, *the daughter of the* KING. *She should be dark, and very intelligent. Historically there are some grounds for the suggestion that she had the Scotch peasant's gift of 'second sight.' She should be beautiful, and rather dignified. She may be dressed in a woollen gown, delicately embroidered.*)

THORGUNNA   Who is the Chief here? I want to see the Chief.

TYRKER   Come with me.

(*He takes her to* LEIF *who is arranging his bedding to dry at his fire. He turns to meet them.*)

THORGUNNA   Are you the Chief of these outlaws?

LEIF   (*With dignity*) There's only one outlaw here, Lady, and

53

that's me. The rest of us are free men and serfs. We aren't an outlaw gang.

THORGUNNA I am sorry, Chief; they told me wrong. Are you the man they call Leif Ericsson?

LEIF That's right. They call me an outlaw, but you don't have to worry about that. I was outlawed with my father when I was a little boy.

THORGUNNA You have committed no crime yourself?

LEIF Lady, what is a crime? In the land I come from we have no set laws; we've never had a Thing. My father had enough of Godis when he was a young man; he won't have one in the place. I can't remember doing anything of which I am ashamed.

THORGUNNA (*Looking at him curiously*) That's a very good answer, Chief.

LEIF Is it?

THORGUNNA Tell me, where do you live? That is really why I came to see you.

LEIF Look, Lady, I appreciate that very much. But when we came here yesterday the King said we might stay here till the wind changed, but we weren't to talk to any of his people. I don't want to get you into trouble, and much more, I don't want you to get us into trouble.

THORGUNNA (*With regal dignity*) I heard about that at our Hall. I am the King's daughter and I have no brothers; one day I shall be the Queen and I shall rule the people of these Isles. My name is Thorgunna.

LEIF Would you care to sit down?

(*She sits down on a heap of furs before his fire; he remains standing in front of her.*)

—What can I tell you, Lady?

THORGUNNA Tell me about the country that you live in. Is it true that you live over to the west of Iceland?

LEIF That's right. Five days west of Iceland you come to our country, but it is wild and desolate in that part; a man could not exist except by hunting seals. From there you sail south along the coast for another five days and turn the corner of the land. There you come to the place where we have our farms.

THORGUNNA Is it a good land? Is it warm, and sunny, and beautiful?

LEIF (*Regretfully*) No, it's not. We always say it is, but it's not really. We can just get a living there, but it's not really much good. (*He looks around the barren Hebridean moorland.*) It's not such a good country as this.

THORGUNNA What is there further west from you? Are there any other lands?

LEIF (*Thoughtfully*) Lady, that's a strange question. This place lies to the west of Norway, and west of this place there is Iceland. If you go west again there is our own country, Greenland, where I come from. When you come to think of it there is no reason why there should not be another land again, westwards of us. I don't believe these stories that the sea comes to an end quite suddenly, and you fall over the edge like falling into a pit.

THORGUNNA I don't believe those, either. But do you know of any other lands, westwards again from your place, where men live?

LEIF I'm sorry, Lady, but I never heard of any lands like that.

THORGUNNA (*Sighs*) No matter. (*She looks around.*) Have your men everything they need? Are you all right for food? I will send you down a sheep.

LEIF Lady, that is a kind thought. They have plenty to eat, but it is dull, dry stuff. They would like fresh meat.

THORGUNNA I will see they get it. (*She gets up to go.*)

LEIF Just one thing, Lady. Why did you ask about land over to the west of us? Is there such a place?

THORGUNNA (*Sitting down again*) I'll tell you. A man came to us from Ireland last summer, a holy man, a monk. He came to tell us all about a new religion, a new way of life. He gave me this. (*She pulls out a small wooden cross from within her dress, suspended on a gold chain round her neck.*) My father does not like it, so I have to keep it hidden.

LEIF (*Curiously*) Is it a talisman?

THORGUNNA It is the sign of a new way of life.

LEIF (*Puzzled*) I'm afraid I don't quite understand.

THORGUNNA No matter. I did not come here to convert you. I was telling you about this holy man. He said that in Ireland, where he came from, they had a legend of a country over to the west, beyond the sea. He called it Hy Breasail, the Happy Land.

LEIF (*Shaking his head*) I have never heard of it.

THORGUNNA It may be that it is not there at all. But if it is, it would be worth while to spend one's whole life looking for it.

LEIF What sort of country is it, Lady?

THORGUNNA If you stand on the edge of the sea looking westwards to the sunset on the evening of a fine day in summer, just after the sun has gone down, you see the sea and the high clouds flushed with pink and gold. Past the horizon and beyond those rosy clouds there lies the Happy Land, which this man called Hy Breasail. No thief, no robber, and no enemy pursues one there;

56

there is no violence, and no winter snow. In that place it is always spring. No flower or lily is wanting, no rose or violet but you will find them there. There apple trees bear flowers and fruit on the same branch, all the year round. There young men live in quiet happiness with their girls; there is no old age, and no sickness, and no sorrow there. All is full of joy . . . (*Her voice dies away.*)

LEIF (*Gently*) Lady, there is no place in the world like that.

THORGUNNA I suppose you're right. I think this monk was mixing up old legends of his country with the Heaven beyond this world that he was telling us about. (*She gets up.*) Thank you for listening to me so patiently, Chief. I will send you down the sheep. (*She turns to go.*)

$\lceil$ DISSOLVE TO:

The Beach

(LEIF *and* TYRKER *are standing together by the ship, watching* THORGUNNA *as she goes away across the hill.*)

LEIF She's going to send us down a sheep this afternoon. We can have fresh meat to-night.

TYRKER That's the best bit of news we've had so far in this stinking hole. I like her better than her father.

LEIF She is the only woman I have ever met who talks intelligently. She is a very clever girl.

TYRKER (*Grinning*) Looks all right, too.

$\lceil$ DISSOLVE TO:

The Beach at Sunrise

(*The ship is seen silhouetted against the dawn sky; one man is awake on watch. In the hencoop a cock crows and the men stir; each man as he wakes looks up at the burgee at the masthead. It is seen blowing straight towards the land.*)

[DISSOLVE TO:

Leif's Camp

(THORGUNNA *is standing with* LEIF *before his tent.*)

LEIF The men are good for nothing this morning, Lady—I can't get any work out of them. They ate too much last night; they ate every bit of that sheep. It was good of you to send it down for them. Next time you'd better send a lamb.

THORGUNNA (*Smiling*) They will want more than that. You may be here for a long time, you know.

LEIF (*Glancing at the burgee at the masthead*) What winds do you get here at this time of year? How long does it go on blowing east like this?

THORGUNNA It blows west in July, but you may be here until the end of June.

LEIF Lady, that's bad news.

THORGUNNA I am sorry.

LEIF (*Worried*) My father sent me on a mission to the King in Norway, but he expects me back this year. If I don't get to Norway till July I shall have to stay the winter there.

THORGUNNA The wind won't change because of that, Leif.

58

LEIF No. (*He stands for a minute, deep in thought.*) There's another thing, Lady. I shall have to be careful that my men don't get into trouble if I keep them here in idleness so long. They're only human, and they are a long way from their homes and from their wives. Will you warn your people to keep their daughters well away from this place? I don't want difficulties of that sort to make your father angry with us.

THORGUNNA I will do that, Leif. It was good of you to think of warning me. We are a hot-blooded people in this island, and your men are very handsome. I will see that no girls come about this place.

LEIF What is this island like? What lies beyond that hill?

THORGUNNA There is a strip of farm-land, and then a quick-running river, full of fish. Beyond that lies the moor where cattle and sheep pasture, and beyond that again there is the mountain and the sea.

LEIF Are the fish fresh-water fish, like they get in Iceland? Can a man eat them?

THORGUNNA We eat them fresh, and salted in the winter. They are very good food.

LEIF Lady, I have a net. It will help my men in this long idleness if they can have a variety of food. Would your father allow me to go to this river with my net, with perhaps one other man to help me with the net, to get some of these fish?

THORGUNNA There is no need to ask my father if I go with you. You'll want somebody who knows the river to show you the best pools. I can do that, and I can help you with the net.

[DISSOLVE TO:

The River

(THORGUNNA *and* LEIF *are shown walking up to the river together. This is a typical Hebridean salmon river, rocky and
fast-running. The scene should be beautiful. The montage
should emphasize the slender dark beauty of the girl in contrast to the blond strength of the man.*)

(*They pause on the bank and study the river. A fish jumps in
the pool.*)

[DISSOLVE TO:

The River

(THORGUNNA *and* LEIF *are shown wading waist-deep in a pool,
one at each side of the river with the net stretched across
between them, working it up the pool. They are intent upon
the water, and moving quietly and stealthily, but they are
smiling; it is great fun.*)

[DISSOLVE TO:

The River Bank

(THORGUNNA *and* LEIF *are dragging the net into a shallow
with a sandy or a flat stone beach, to get the fish ashore. They
pull it in; it has perhaps one salmon and a few parr or trout
in it. They crouch down together by the water's edge to examine their catch. This scene should be sunny and beautiful.*)

THORGUNNA These little ones with spots are very sweet; I like them best, myself. But your men are so big—(*She glances at* LEIF *shyly.*)—that I think they will like the big ones better.

LEIF   They are grand fish. We catch fish in the sea, but not so good as these. We have no fishing of this sort at home.

THORGUNNA   Are there no rivers in your country?

LEIF   None like this. You'd think our country was a poor place if you came to visit it.

THORGUNNA   (*Looking round over the wild Hebridean scenery.*) Is your country much worse than ours?

LEIF   Most of it is covered in ice and snow all the year round. We tell everybody that it's the best land in the world, and we get along all right there, but it's not so good as this. I don't mind you knowing.

THORGUNNA   (*Wistfully*) I want to travel some day and see other places. I do envy you, going to Norway. They say it's a wonderful country. The trees there grow seventy or eighty feet high in the valleys.

LEIF   No!

THORGUNNA   It's quite true. I'd like to go there and see trees like that. I'd like to see your Greenland, too.

LEIF   You wouldn't like Greenland. It's not a good country.

THORGUNNA   (*Thoughtfully*) A good country is a country where there are good people, a place where men are kind, and generous, and simple. I think your country is a better one than this. (*She rouses, and picks up the net.*) There is a good pool down below that rapid, but we must get over to the other bank.

(*They turn and splash knee-deep through the water, laughing together.* LEIF *takes her hand to help her through a deep bit.*)

61

Hill Overlooking Leif's Camp

(*It is evening.* THORGUNNA *and* LEIF *come up to the crest and see the ship upon the beach below them, and the camp, not very far away.* LEIF *is carrying the net upon his back; it is full of fish. They stop on the crest of the hill.*)

THORGUNNA I will not come down to the camp with you; I will go home from here.

LEIF (*Taking her hand*) Lady, I have to thank you for two things; for these fish, and for a very happy day. Shall we meet again?

THORGUNNA I know where there are seagulls' eggs on the rock face. Do your men like those?

LEIF Lady, my chaps will eat anything from seaweed to a bit of walrus hide. If they could get eggs now and then it would be fine.

THORGUNNA I can show you where those are, if you like. We might meet out here.

LEIF To-morrow—two hours after sunrise?

(*They smile at each other.*)

The Cliff

(LEIF *and* THORGUNNA *are seen clambering about on the face of a cliff, with the sea beating upon rocks hundreds of feet below them. The effect should be one of terrifying height. They do not consider it dangerous; they have a woven fish basket with them and they are gathering seagulls' eggs. They are chatting and laughing together.*)

LEIF   There's a slippery bit here; be careful how you come.

THORGUNNA   Be careful yourself, or else give me the eggs.

LEIF   (*Looking at the sea far below him*) If I fell down there I don't suppose I'd worry much about the eggs. I might bounce once upon that sticking out bit, but then it's a clear drop down to the rocks.

(THORGUNNA *is standing on a rocky ledge. She is leaning a little against the rock wall behind her, and she is staring at the far horizon, motionless. All the gaiety has gone from her, and her face is set and expressionless.*)

THORGUNNA   Leif, you mustn't fall.

LEIF   (*Turning to look at her*) Of course not. Hullo—what's the matter?

THORGUNNA   (*Motionless*) You mustn't fall.
   (LEIF *goes to her quickly, and takes her hand.*)

LEIF   Thorgunna, what's the matter? Are you feeling queer?

THORGUNNA   (*Looking down at his hand holding hers*) I—I don't quite know.

LEIF   We'll sit and rest a bit. This isn't a very good place to feel faint, you know. Wake up.

THORGUNNA   (*Passing her hand over her eyes*) I'm all right. I thought . . . oh, I don't know what I thought.

LEIF   We'll knock off for a bit, and get up to the cliff top, and sit down.

63

THORGUNNA If you like.

[DISSOLVE TO :

The Cliff Top

(*This is an open, grassy slope high above the sea, sunny and windswept.* THORGUNNA *and* LEIF *are sitting close together.*)

LEIF What happened down there, Thorgunna? Did you feel ill?

THORGUNNA No—not ill. I just got a—a sort of feeling that you mustn't fall. It seemed to be so urgent . . . suddenly. (*Turns to him*) I don't suppose you can understand.

LEIF (*Grinning*) I've a kind of idea that I do.

THORGUNNA (*Laughing*) It wasn't that. It wasn't anything to do with us. (*Seriously*) It was bigger than that. It seemed to be terribly important, suddenly, that nothing should happen to you. Not only to me.

LEIF (*Puzzled*) Who to, then?

THORGUNNA (*With wonder in her voice*) Sort of—to the world. To every man and every woman still unborn, living in countries far beyond our own that we know nothing about. It seemed to me that if you fell, something would be lost to all those unborn people we shall never know, and God would grieve for them, and I should grieve with God.

LEIF You're a queer girl, Thorgunna.

THORGUNNA That's what they used to say about my mother.

LEIF I never met any one like you before. I never before met any woman that I could—respect.

64

THORGUNNA (*Gravely*) If I repeated that it would sound silly, but it would be true.

LEIF (*Putting his arm round her shoulders*) Tell me, what was it you were thinking about me before you went all funny on the cliff?

[DISSOLVE TO:

The Hayfield

(*This is a low field beside the sea; the western beach runs up to this field so that you look out over the sea towards the sunset. The hay is cut and in stacks upon the field, ready for carting the next day. It is evening. LEIF and THORGUNNA are standing hand-in-hand looking at the sunset, silhouetted against it. This is a very beautiful scene.*) •

LEIF Beyond those clouds, you say there lies the Happy Land. What was its name?

THORGUNNA Hy Breasail. The land beyond the sunset, the place where everything is clean and beautiful and good.

LEIF The Happy Land. Surely, the place where you are happy is that Happy Land.

(*He slips his arm around her shoulders; she smiles up at him. They turn again and look at the glory of the sunset.*)

THORGUNNA It's lovely, Leif. Let's sit and watch it for a bit. You haven't got to go back yet, have you?

LEIF Not yet.

(*They sit down together with their backs against a haycock, LEIF with his arm around her shoulders, watching the sunset.*

The colours change and deepen; a star or two shows in the sky. The colours glow and fade till there is only a thin gold streak against the deep blue sky, pierced with a thousand stars.)

LEIF (*Gently*) You haven't got to go back yet, have you?

THORGUNNA Not yet.

[FADE TO:

The Camp

(*Daytime;* LEIF *and* TYRKER *are looking at the burgee at the masthead of the ship. It is blowing away from the land, in the reverse direction to the previous shots of it.*)

LEIF Well, we've got our west wind at last. We've been here over a month.

TYRKER (*Sourly*) We've been here seven weeks.

LEIF Not so long as that, surely?

TYRKER We got here on the twenty-fifth of May. This is the fifth of July.

LEIF It hasn't seemed like seven weeks.

TYRKER It's seemed like seven years to all the rest of us. We haven't all got—

LEIF That's enough of that. Do you think this wind is settled in the west?

TYRKER (*Looking round the sky*) I think so. The sky looks quite different now. It's got much warmer. I think it will be west now for some days.

66

LEIF (*Heavily*) All right, we'll sail at dawn. Tell the men; get everything cleaned up and on board to-night. It's high water about two in the morning; we'll float off on that, and lie at anchor till the dawn.

TYRKER (*Gently*) You will have other business to attend to. I will see to everything.

LEIF All right. I am going to the town now, to see the King, to tell him we are leaving.

[DISSOLVE TO:

The King's Hall

(*This is a wooden building with a high, vaulted roof. It should be larger than any building we have seen so far but not enormous, because later in the story the hall of King Olaf in Norway has to be very much larger. It has one or two long benches for meals, a sleeping dais at one end, and near this dais a large open fireplace. The KING is seated on the dais, informally, with a number of his warriors about him; they are all heavily armed, and are real toughs. There are one or two very fierce, large dogs about the place that snarl as LEIF speaks and are held back by the men. LEIF stands before the KING.*)

LEIF Sir, the wind has changed, and we can get away for Norway with the dawn. We have been here for seven weeks. I am sorry that we had to stay so long. I want to thank you for allowing us to camp here, both for myself and also for my father who sent me on this mission.

KING I want no thanks from an outlaw. Still, you have behaved yourselves and made no trouble. Lucky for you. If you had started messing with our women I would have slaughtered the whole lot

67

of you; not one man would have got away to boast of it. However, go with my goodwill. Tell King Olaf, when you see him, that I keep this country clean.

LEIF   I shall tell him that, sir. I shall tell him that you keep this country as clean as our own.

KING   (*Fiercely*) You are insolent.

LEIF   I meant no insult, sir. But we are a proud people, too.

KING   (*Sinking back*) Go in peace, before I change my mind. Get out.

[DISSOLVE TO:

Leif's Camp

(*It is almost dark; there is a thin band of sunset light still showing in the night sky to the west. The tents have been struck and the camp site has been cleared except for the fire which was in front of* LEIF's *tent; this is still burning, and* LEIF *is sitting by it; there are one or two packages of his personal goods still there, and some furs.*)

(THORGUNNA *walks in from the darkness.* LEIF *gets up to meet her.*)

LEIF   I am glad you have come down. If you had not, I would have come up to your window in the night and tapped on it, because I had to see you. My dear, we sail at dawn; the wind is fair for Norway.

THORGUNNA   I know; I heard about it at the Hall this afternoon. You went to see my father. He is glad that you are leaving. (*She sits down on a heap of furs before the fire.*)

68

LEIF He hates the sight of me.

THORGUNNA He hates everybody. (*Turns to him*) Leif, I want you to take me away with you in your ship, to Norway.

LEIF Does your father know anything about this?

THORGUNNA No. I wouldn't dare to tell him.

LEIF Oh . . .

(*There is a pause. He stares at the fire, considering. She glances at him.*)

—I've been thinking about this. If we were free people, you should come with me to Norway and beyond, Thorgunna.

THORGUNNA (*Puzzled*) We are free to do what we want to.

LEIF No, we're not. You are the most high-born lady in this land, and I'm an outlaw. Your father would kill me if I asked for you in marriage. If I carry you off with me, he will come after us; in this poor ship I cannot get away beyond the range of his galleys. I cannot fight your father's warriors, and we so few in number. If I try that, I and all my people with me will be killed in battle. Back in Greenland, the wives of all these men will wait for them until they sink down mourning. That is the truth of it.

THORGUNNA I never thought about the galleys. I think you're right in one thing; my father would do everything he could to have you killed.

LEIF If I were here as a lone man I'd take the chance. But, Thorgunna, I'm on a mission for my father. Back home in Greenland, people depend on what I can achieve for them in Norway, and I've got to get there. (*Pause*) My dear, I can't take you with me in the ship.

THORGUNNA I don't think that's the right decision, Leif.

LEIF (*Heavily*) Thorgunna, as one goes through life one has to make the best decisions that one can, and work on them. You can't do more than your best. I've thought this over a long time, and that is how I'm going to take it.

THORGUNNA You don't know all the facts for your decision. I'm no longer a lone woman, Leif. I'm going to have a baby, and it's yours.

LEIF (*Smiling*) I wondered about that. (*He slips his arm round her shoulders, and kisses her.*) It looks as though this decision has been made for us, after all. You shall stay here to-night; we sail at dawn. We will declare our marriage at King Olaf's court. You'll have to come just as you are. I have some rough, men's clothes that you can wear; we'll get a proper outfit for you when we get to Norway.

THORGUNNA (*Shivering*) Leif, my father will come after us. He's a terrible man when he is angry.

LEIF I have a black hen in the hencoop, that I brought with me in case we got into a jam. I will make a sacrifice, and ask Odin to send a fog.

THORGUNNA Leif, there is one God only, and He is not Odin. Killing your black hen will do no good. My father will come after us, and we shall all be killed in battle.

LEIF He would never kill you.

THORGUNNA I think he would.

(*They sit together silent for a minute. The leaping flames illuminate their faces; there is dark, velvety blackness behind them.*)

THORGUNNA (*Much distressed*) Leif, I want to tell you something. Some of my people have the gift of second sight. My mother said once that I would bear a son to a strange man who came up from the sea. We all laughed about it at the time, but now I think that she was right. I can see things in the smoke clouds sometimes, Leif.

LEIF (*Shocked*) You mustn't go playing with that sort of thing. It brings you in touch with devils.

THORGUNNA I haven't done it since the holy man came from Ireland, because he said that it was wrong. But as for devils, Leif, I never saw much harm in anything that happened. Ought I to try to see what lies ahead of us? I think I might get something that would help.

LEIF (*Gently*) I don't know much about these things. I never saw a devil myself; perhaps there aren't any, really. Go ahead and do it, if it will help you, Thorgunna.

THORGUNNA (*Distressed*) The holy man said that if I did it again it would bring damnation to my soul.

LEIF I should leave it alone.

THORGUNNA Do you think I might just ask Mother?

LEIF I didn't know you had a mother. Where is she?

THORGUNNA She is dead. She died last year.

LEIF Oh . . .

THORGUNNA (*Slightly offended*) You don't have to be afraid of Mother; she's not a devil. She was kind, and good, and very, very wise.

LEIF (*Uneasily*) What have you got to do?

THORGUNNA (*Showing him a satchel*) I brought the things down with me. It's only a matter of burning a few of these dead leaves and rare herbs in the fire to make a smoke. And I must sing the Warlocks' Song.

71

LEIF (*Very uneasily*) The Warlocks' Song . . . That calls up spirits from the grave. (*Instinctively he loosens a dagger at his belt.*)

THORGUNNA (*Sadly*) There is nothing to fear. You will see nothing but a silly, frightened girl staring at the smoke that she is making in the fire, and singing a little.

(*She begins to throw the herbs and leaves from her satchel into the fire; smoke begins to rise and wreathe about them. LEIF sits tense, his hand upon his dagger. In the background, in the semidarkness. TWO MEN working at the moorings of the ship look up and notice what is going on. They stare appalled, leave their work, and hurry off into the ship in superstitious awe. The smoke swirls up and thickens to a dense screen.*)

THORGUNNA (*Chants*) Come now, my mother,
       From the shadow of the Holy Tree;
      Help me with vision
      And show me my way.

(*The wreathing smoke turns to a wet mist, grows thin, and gradually discloses Niagara Falls, shot from somewhere at the bottom. The scene merges to an interior shot of the power station at the bottom and a turbo generator running; a close up of the rotor gradually fills the screen with a whirl of machinery, changing back into the wreathing smoke.*)

(*THORGUNNA, puzzled, passes a hand across her eyes and throws more herbs into the fire. Again the smoke swirls up as a dense screen.*)

THORGUNNA (*Chants*) From Yggdrasil, come
       To succour your daughter
      That the Power of the Wise Ones
      May help me in danger.

(*Upon the background of the smoke slowly appears a shot of* LEIF *talking to the Scotch slave,* HAKI, *who comes later in the story. They are examining some ears of wheat that the Scot has brought. The scene merges to a panorama of a vast wheat-field in the Middle West at harvest time. A large reaper and binder comes straight at the camera, noisy and terrifying.* THORGUNNA *gives a slight cry, and the scene merges back into smoke.*)

(THORGUNNA *is very distressed, and rubs her eyes again.*)

LEIF (*Uneasily*) Is it nearly over?

THORGUNNA (*Distressed*) I am only allowed one more, and I can't understand what it all means.

(*She throws her last handful of herbs into the fire. Again the smoke wreathes up to form a curtain.*)

THORGUNNA (*Chants*) Mother, give me a clue
                 That will help me to-night,
          So that that which I do
               May be wise in your sight—
                    Mother, help me.

(*The smoke clouds wreathe apart and disclose a shot of New York City from across the waters of the harbour, not clear cut, but a sunlit scene seen through a film of smoke. This merges in a swirl of smoke to a repeat of the shots of Niagara, the power station, and the wheatfield, and then to a shot of* LEIF *at the steering oar of his ship in a rough sea. Finally this merges to a head and shoulders shot of an old lady,* THOR-GUNNA's *mother; she nods slightly, without smiling.*)

(*The smoke grows thin and dies down, disclosing the wood fire and the stone hearth, and the black night beyond.* THOR-GUNNA *is exhausted with mental strain, she passes a hand wearily across her eyes.*)

73

LEIF (*Hoarsely*) What did you see?

THORGUNNA (*Piteously*) I don't understand. It must have all meant something. There was a waterfall, but so enormous that it never could have been; it was as if all the sea was pouring down into one place. Then there was a sort of whirling thing, in a house. It might have been a temple. Then I saw you talking to an uncouth man about some ears of wheat, and then it was all wheat as far as one could see, more wheat than all the people in the world could eat. And then there was a dragon. There was an island with stone houses like tall cliffs, taller than any house could ever be, all white and shining in the sun. You were mixed up in all of them in some way, Leif, because I saw you in your ship. And I saw Mother.

LEIF Were you with me in the ship?

THORGUNNA (*Sadly*) No. I wasn't with you.

LEIF (*Gently*) Don't think about it any more now. Lie down here for a bit, and try and get some sleep. I'll wake you when it's time to go on board.

THORGUNNA I *must* think about it. I've done this several times before and it has always made sense in the end, even if one didn't understand it just at first.

LEIF You'll have a quiet time to think it over in the ship. Lie down now and rest.

THORGUNNA (*Slowly*) Leif, I'm not coming with you in the ship.

LEIF Not coming with me?

THORGUNNA No. I do not understand what I have seen but I know this about it; that there is no evil in it, that in some way it concerns your destiny, that it is terribly important, and that it is

74

true. You must go on alone without me, and do what you have to do.

LEIF But you can come with me.

THORGUNNA (*Getting to her feet*) If I come with you, you and all your people will be killed in battle with my father. If it were ourselves only, we might take the chance, for life without each other isn't going to be much fun. But there's more in it than that.

(*She is standing now, and speaking regally. She is no longer a shy girl, but a responsible woman and the daughter of a king.*)

—I do not understand what I have learned about your fate, but I know this about it. It is more important than you, or I, or anybody in this place. I will not tamper with such matters, Leif, or bring about your death before you have fulfilled your destiny. You must go on alone. I shall stay here.

LEIF What will your father do when he finds out about the baby?

THORGUNNA He will be very angry, but he will not dare to hurt me or your son. I shall not tell him till some months have passed.

LEIF Thorgunna, all this is based on fancies, wreaths of the wood smoke, no more than that. Come down to earth. We can get away soon after midnight and be well clear of the island before dawn. We'll sail out to the north; your father will not think of that. Let's go on board now.

THORGUNNA No. I am not coming with you.

LEIF Is that your firm decision?

THORGUNNA Yes.

LEIF Then I say this to you. (*He takes a gold ring from his finger and gives it to her.*) Take my ring, and when your child is born

75

show them this ring and say that I, Leif Ericsson, am father of your child, and I acknowledge it.

THORGUNNA I will do that, Leif. This child that I shall bear for you will be a son. When he is old enough to travel I will send him to you in Greenland.

LEIF I will treat him as my very son. (*He turns to one of his packs and produces a belt of walrus tusks and shows it to her.*) My father sent this belt as one of the presents that I was to give to King Olaf. Walrus tusks have a strong charm; a belt like this makes the wearer valiant and manly. I think it is a better present for my son. Give it to him, and let him wear it when he comes to me in Greenland, so that I may know it is my own son and no other.

THORGUNNA (*Taking the belt*) I will do that, Leif. Some day when I can get away from here, I will come to you in Greenland myself.

LEIF My dear, I shall be waiting for you.

(*They kiss.*)

—You are shivering.

THORGUNNA It has turned cold.

LEIF (*Taking off his cloak and putting it around her shoulders.*) Take this coat of mine. It is good Greenland frieze, woven at home; we have cold winters there.

THORGUNNA (*Gratefully*) You are a good man, Leif. Before the end, I shall come to you in Greenland.

[FADE TO:

The Classroom

CALLENDER She did have a son, and she sent the boy to Leif

76

in Greenland as soon as he was old enough to travel; he was called Thorgils, and Leif acknowledged him as his son and brought him up. Thorgunna did not get away for a long time. Many years later, when she was growing old, she started out to go to Leif in Greenland. Travelling was hard and difficult for people in those days. Thorgunna died in Iceland, while she was waiting for a ship to take her on to Greenland to her lover. She never saw Leif again. (*He turns to the map and indicates.*) Leif sailed away from the Hebrides, here, and round the north of Scotland, and over to the coast of Norway, here. And so he came to the court of King Olaf.

[CUT TO:

The Next Room

(*In the next classroom the* HEADMASTER *is looking very glum.*)

HEADMASTER   All this is quite unsuitable for boys.

[FADE TO:

King Olaf's Hall

(*The scene is a vast wooden hall, with a high, pitched roof, rather like a college hall. It should be a busy place, full of people going about domestic tasks. There may be a long sleeping bench at one end; near this would be an enormous fireplace with a huge log fire. The body of the hall may be occupied by a couple of tables running the full length, with benches. At the end remote from the dais these tables may be used for various domestic tasks; thus there may be a man sharpening a scythe, another repairing harness, a third making some article of wooden furniture, etc. Later on, the two Scotch slaves will be seen eating at this end of the hall amongst all this litter, indicating their debased social position.*)

(KING OLAF *may be a middle-aged, intelligent man, seated in a richly carved wooden chair before the fire. Behind him there stand one or two of his counsellors, amongst them a monk.* LEIF *stands before the* KING, *and behind him is* TYRKER *with one or two other men from the ship. They have brought with them a number of sacks of furs and odd parcels.*)

KING OLAF   You are the son of Eric the Red?

LEIF   Yes, King.

KING OLAF   I know all about your father. He was outlawed from this country for manslaughter, and again from North Iceland, and a third time from South Iceland. Then he sailed away and settled somewhere far over to the west. Is that right?

LEIF   It is quite right, King. He sent me to you, to tell you about the affairs of our country.

KING OLAF   I shall be glad to hear them. Does your father still fight as much as ever?

LEIF   No—he's getting a bit old for that. He went back once to Iceland and had a fight with Thorgest and got beaten up. After that he gave up fighting.

KING OLAF   I dare say. It's not so much fun fighting when you can't win any longer. What has he to say to me?

LEIF   King, we are living on our farms in a vast country. There are two hundred of us there, but we all live together in one corner; no man knows how big the country is. We know this; in length it is at least six days' sailing from north to south with a fair wind. It is probably nearly as wide.

78

KING OLAF (*Impressed*) I had no idea it was as big as that.

LEIF It is an enormous country, King. We run it properly, too. Technically, sir, we are an outlaw settlement, and we have no rights. But we have lived now for fifteen years upon our farms in this new country; we have lived peaceably, with few quarrels and no murder. We are as clean and decent a crowd as any others in your domains.

KING OLAF I expect that's true enough. I don't suppose that anybody cares to start an argument with your father. (*He looks at* LEIF *thoughtfully*) Or with you, either.

LEIF My father rules the country well, without violence; men are happy under him.

KING OLAF (*Laughing*) All right; I'll take your word for it. What did he send you to say to me?

LEIF King, he sent me to ask if you would accept our country as a formal colony. We cannot carry on upon our own. We have used up the few manufactured things we brought with us from Iceland, sir; we need your support. We need iron goods, plough-shares, nails, axe heads, and things like that, and we need timber, for our country grows no trees. We can give you in exchange furs of every sort, and walrus hides, and sea ivory, and sometimes we find ambergris. I have samples of these things here with me. May I show them to you?

KING OLAF Have them unwrapped.

(LEIF *motions to* TYRKER, *who begins to undo the parcels with the men from the ship.*)

—You have stated your case clearly and well, Ericsson. Are you an educated person? Can you read and write?

LEIF No. We can none of us do that in Greenland.

(KING OLAF *gets up and crosses over to the goods which are being unpacked.*)

KING OLAF   Why do you call your country Greenland? Is it so green and fertile?

LEIF   Well, as a matter of fact, it's not. Most of it is covered in snow all the year round, and although it's not particularly mountainous the middle of it is certainly very high. We can just rub along by hunting and farming in the corner where we are; it would be easier if we had more people. My father says that Iceland was called by a bad name, because nobody wants to go to a place where it's all ice and snow. He said that we should call our country Greenland, so that people would want to come and settle there.

KING OLAF   (*Laughing*) Well, that makes sense. You are more intelligent than most of my subjects.

LEIF   I am honoured, sir.

KING OLAF   (*Examining the goods*) These things are quite good quality. We can take all that you can send us of these—and we can sell these for you in France, and get good prices. It's all quite useful stuff, if you can make delivery in big enough quantities to make it worth while. What exactly do you want me to do?

LEIF   We want you to send out a ship each year loaded with iron goods and timber in exchange for a cargo of these things.

KING OLAF   (*Thoughtfully*) I see. (*He muses for a moment, and then looks at* LEIF.) And I suppose you want me to cancel your outlawry, and to confirm you as the rulers of your Greenland?

LEIF   Yes, King.

KING OLAF   I will think it over and discuss it with my council. What are your plans? Can you get back this year?

LEIF   No. I shall have to stay in this country now until the wind blows east in the spring.

80

KING OLAF You may stay in my court as my guest. You are an intelligent fellow; I shall want to have more talk with you during the winter.

LEIF You are gracious to an outlaw, sir.

KING OLAF I'll do something about that, anyway.

[FADE TO:

A Room in a Shipwright's House

(*Little need be shown of this room except a table with a bench or two. LEIF is sitting deep in study with a master shipwright; there are parchment drawings on the table, and a model of a knorr, or merchant ship; there may be one or two samples of woollen sail fabric, and cordage.*)

LEIF (*Handling the model*) Our difficulty will be with the keel; we shall never have timber of that length. Can we joint it?

SHIPWRIGHT I have a drawing here; you can joint it only in this way. If you join keel members any other way than this, your ship will break in a rough sea.

(*They bend together over the design. A MAN comes in at the door behind them; his clothing is lightly powdered with snow.*)

MAN Is Leif Ericsson here?

LEIF I am Ericsson.

MAN King Olaf wants you. He is in the Great Hall.

[DISSOLVE TO:

King Olaf's Hall

(*The* KING *is sitting by the fire; there is a vacant chair beside him. There are no other people near at hand, though the hall is busy as before.* LEIF *comes in wearing a cloak, which is lightly powdered with snow. He stands before the* KING.)

KING OLAF Sit down, Ericsson.

(LEIF *throws off his cloak and sits down on the vacant chair.*)

KING OLAF I have thought over your matter for some weeks now, and I have discussed it with my council. Before I tell you what we have decided, I want you to answer a few more questions.

LEIF Everything I know is at your service, King.

KING OLAF First, do you know of any other countries, westward again from you, beyond the land you live in now?

LEIF (*Slowly*) I do not know of any. Yet . . .

KING OLAF Yet what?

LEIF I did once meet a woman who believed in such a place. She called it Hy Breasail.

KING OLAF (*Smiling*) I know that one. Hy Breasail, the Happy Land, the land where it is summer all the time and nobody grows old?

LEIF Sir, that is what she said.

KING OLAF Do you believe in such a place?

LEIF (*Slowly*) No. I do not think that we shall ever find a land like that. But just as our land lies to the west of Iceland, so there may quite well be another land, westwards again from us.

KING OLAF I think so, too. Frankly, Leif Ericsson, I do not like what I have heard of this Greenland that you come from.

It was a bold venture to go there, and your father has done well. I do not think that you will ever work it up into an important colony; the country is too much against you. If I help you now and send the ship each year that you have asked me for, it is because I look upon you as an outpost of my Empire, as a spearhead. (*Earnestly*) There *must* be new lands, westwards of you again. The world does not come to an end at a sharp edge, as these crackpot philosophers try to tell me. There are other lands beyond the sea, westwards of you. They may be better ones than any that we know.

LEIF If so, they would lie somewhat to the south of us. Our land is too darned cold. That's all there is against it.

KING OLAF South, or southwest of you. I am going to support your colony, and I will send the ship each year. But if I do so, you must mind my word. As opportunity occurs you are to venture further to the west and south. I do not think that you will find Hy Breasail in your travelling, till that last travel that we all must take. But you may find good countries, nonetheless.

LEIF I will remember all that you have said, and I will tell my father your commands. He's getting a bit old, but it will be no burden to me to adventure further into the unknown.

KING OLAF No—you are still young. Now, if I give you my support, there are certain changes that I shall require. First, do you know this sign?

(*He shows a wooden cross, not a crucifix. It is quite plain, but very well made.*)

LEIF I met a woman once who showed me one of those. It is a talisman.

KING OLAF You seem to have met some interesting women for so young a man. It is not a talisman. It is the sign of a new religion, the faith in the Lord Jesus who gave His life for you and for all men. It is the sign of a new way of life.

83

LEIF So I have heard.

KING OLAF We call the men of this religion Christians, from the name of our Lord, Jesus Christ. I became Christian two years ago, with all my people; this priest that you have seen about the place is a Christian priest, sent to me from Rome. I will not have a pagan colony in my domains. You must take this priest to Greenland with you in your ship to teach the new religion in your country, and you must stop worshipping the old gods, Thor and Odin. And you must give up sacrifices.

LEIF Can't we even sacrifice a cock for a fair wind? It's going to make navigation very difficult if we can't do that.

KING OLAF There are to be no more sacrifices at all. You'll find you get along just as well without them.

LEIF Maybe. I was never a religious man, King, and these things don't mean a great deal to me, personally. (*He sits for a moment deep in thought.*) I think there will be some difficulty in altering the religion of our people. You see, my father was a fighting man. Now in his old age he has got quite religious, but he likes a religion with a bit of blood and fighting in it. I do not think this Jesus-cult would satisfy him at all.

KING OLAF Nevertheless, that is my will. (*He eyes* LEIF *shrewdly.*) I would not send a ship each year out to a pagan colony.

LEIF (*Smiling*) I am sure that argument will have great weight with my father. I will put it to him in that light.

KING OLAF Good. You are to take the priest back with you, and everybody in the country is to listen to his teaching and become Christian, and obey him in religious matters. I know that a man of your wit and ability can pull this off if he gives his mind to it.

LEIF I'll do what I can. It's not going to be easy; you must warn

84

the priest that he may get a rough passage for the first few months. Our people are conservative. You must give us full support in everything we do.

KING OLAF   You shall have it.

LEIF   May I take a written parchment back with me saying that we are to be Christians, stamped with your royal seal, sir? Our people won't be able to read it, but they'll like to see the seal, particularly if it's a big, red one.

KING OLAF   I will have it prepared for you; the priest can read it to them. You must build the priest a church, that he may teach the people in it. I will give him all the furnishings to take with him.

LEIF   Sir, that shall be done.

KING OLAF   Now for another thing. I do not think you know enough about the country that you live in, how large it is, or what it can produce in places that you have not visited. I sent one of my galleys to raid Scotland this year to pick up some sheep; they brought a few slaves back with them. (*He glances up at the membrane-covered window.*) Take a look out of the door and tell me if the snow has stopped.

(*LEIF goes to the door of the hall, and returns.*)

LEIF   It has stopped snowing, and the clouds are breaking over to the west.

KING OLAF   (*Getting up*) Come with me.

(*They put on cloaks and go out of the hall into the snow-covered streets. KING OLAF takes LEIF to a sort of farmyard with a midden in the middle. At one corner of this there is a small hut. A farm-hand comes forward with a key and unlocks the door of this hut for them; they go in.*)

The Hut

(*Inside, this little hut is furnished with a fire in an open hearth, some piles of straw for bedding, and not much else. In it are the two Scotch SLAVES. The man, HAKI, is standing and bows awkwardly as they come in. The GIRL stays crouched upon the straw in the background, not in fear, but in shyness. That is HAEKIA.*)

(*Both are very young, about sixteen or seventeen years old. They speak with a slight Scotch accent. They are slim and wiry young people. They are as shy as wild animals, and they have the natural grace of animals. They are clearly of a much lower order of civilization than the Norsemen. The Norsemen treat them kindly, like animals.*)

(*They are dressed each in a single garment of skin, with the fur inside. This has a hood, and is sleeveless. It is knee long, and buttons between the legs. There is a long slit down from each armhole which can be buttoned for warmth or left open for ventilation. This one garment is dressed or painted white, as a sign of slavery. For the same reason their hair is cut short.*)

KING OLAF These are the two Scotch slaves that I was telling you about. The man is called Haki and the woman Haekia.

LEIF (*Curiously*) Are they man and wife?

KING OLAF I don't think they've got around to that just yet. You'd better marry them when they're a bit older. I am going to give them to you.

LEIF Sir, this is a noble gift.

KING OLAF They can run further and faster than anybody in the world; they are swifter than deer. Take them with you when you go back to Greenland and send them running out over your new country, and any other new countries that you may discover.

Then send word back to me each year by the ship, to say how big your countries are, and what they produce.

LEIF   I will do that. The priest can write a letter for us.

KING OLAF   By the time the priest has done with you, you'll be able to write a letter for yourself. (*They laugh.*) I will show you what these Scots can do. (*He turns to* HAKI.) You know Raudulf in the Osterdal valley?

HAKI   Ay, sir, I mind him well.

KING OLAF   Go to him quickly, and ask him how many cows he has, how many bulls, how many pigs, and how many sheep. Ask how many of each he has now, and how many of each have died since he came to see me here last summer. You understand what I want to know?

HAKI   Ay, sir.

KING OLAF   Then go on to Sigurd in the Haukboer and ask him to give you the horse bridle that I lent him in the fall, and bring it back to me.

HAKI   Ay, Lord. We will gae quick.

KING OLAF   How long will it take you?

(HAKI *turns to the girl and speaks to her in Gaelic; she uncurls from the straw and stands up. They talk in Gaelic for a moment.*)

HAKI   It will be gloaming, Lord. We shall be back by dark.

KING OLAF   Will you take food with you?

HAKI   Lord, food makes us heavy. We will eat when we get back.

(*They set off from the door of the hut, running out over the snow-covered fields, side by side. They run at a steady pace for they have a long way to go. The* KING *and* LEIF *stand to-*

87

gether by the door of the hut watching till they vanish in the distance.)

LEIF How far is it?

KING OLAF From here to Osterdal is fourteen miles, and six from Osterdal to Haukboer. The round trip is about thirty-four miles.

LEIF Why did you send them both?

KING OLAF The country is not easy, and one helps the other. (*Laughs*) I remember one of my herdsmen once, got half way up a cliff and couldn't get up or down. I had to go and get him down myself. It's better to send two.

[DISSOLVE TO:

The Journey

(*A series of scenes without dialogue showing* HAKI *and* HAEKIA *on this journey. The country is wild moorland and forest, partly snow covered. The Scots are running barefoot, steady and purposeful. In one place they have to wade a torrent, in another they go by a goat path over a steep crag. Emphasis should be laid upon the way in which they help each other at these difficult places. In general,* HAEKIA *should be shown in the lead, to balance her shyness in society.*)

[DISSOLVE TO:

King Olaf's Hall

(*An evening scene; the hall is lit by torches, so that it is filled with a haze of smoke.* LEIF *is sitting with the* KING *before the fire of huge wood logs. A* MAN *comes to them.*)

MAN King, the two Scots are at the door.

KING OLAF Bring them in.

(*He glances at a thick candle burning by the hearth, roughly marked off in inch lengths, and turns to* LEIF.)

—About six hours.

LEIF They have been very quick.

(*The* SCOTS *are brought forward, and stand together before the* KING. *They are flushed and sweating a little, and splashed with mud, but they are not unduly distressed.* HAKI *carries a crude bridle in his hand, and* HAEKIA *has a number of small skin bags.*)

KING OLAF You saw Sigurd?

HAKI Lord, he sent this bridle. (*He gives it to the* KING.) He said to tell you that the waters are out at Jotunheim and the little bridge is down, but the river has stopped rising.

KING OLAF Good. And Raudulf?

HAKI (*To* HAEKIA) The beasts first.

(*She gives him one of the little bags. They go down on their knees on the stone floor before the* KING *and open it, and spread out thirty-eight white pebbles and three black ones from the bag.* HAKI *points to the black pebbles.*)

—Lord, these are the bulls he has, one stone for each. (*Points to the white ones*) These are the cows, one stone for each. None have died.

LEIF I make that thirty-eight cows, sir.

KING OLAF That's just about what he should have.

(HAKI *opens another bag and shows three black pebbles and five white ones, and nine bits of slate. He puts the slates on one side.*)

HAKI Lord, these slates are for the pigs that died; they had pig sickness, very bad. These are the boars now living, and these the sows. He thinks the sickness is over now.

(HAEKIA *opens the last bag and shows seven bits of slate, fifty-four white stones, and eight black ones.*)

HAEKIA Lord, these are the sheep that died, and these the rams that he has now, and these the ewes.

KING OLAF Good. Did you find much snow upon the road? Did you see any animals?

HAKI By Haukboer the snow is deep, but for the rest of the way it was not deeper than it is here, Lord. There is much water in the second river between here and Osterdal. Between Osterdal and Haukboer near the forest there were tracks of very many deer; they had been there to-day, but we saw one only.

KING OLAF You have done very well. Go now, and eat, and wash yourselves; you must not go to sleep with all that mud on you.

HAKI (*Obediently*) No, Lord.

KING OLAF (*Signing to an attendant*) Give them food and ale, as much as they can eat.

(*The* SCOTS *are led away.*)

LEIF King, may I go and talk to them when they have eaten?

KING OLAF By all means. They are now your slaves.

(*Cut to a scene of the* SCOTS *at the conclusion of their meal. They eat with their hands, of course, but not with excessive*

90

crudity. They have eaten a good deal, and there are many bones upon their platters. There is a pewter jug of ale before them, and they drink from earthenware flagons.)

(*They are seated alone at the lowest bench in the hall, at the very far end from the* KING, *amongst the litter of handwork at that end. A camera effect of their isolation at the extreme end of a long table in the vast hall should show their social grade. It may be emphasized by* LEIF *walking down the whole length of the hall to them. He sits down informally on a bench beside them.*)

LEIF Haki, did you understand what the King said this morning? He has given Haekia and you to me. My name is Leif, the son of Eric.

HAKI Ay, sir, we ken that.

LEIF I am very glad to have you, because you are clever people, and you run better than anybody I have ever heard of. The King says I am to take you to the country that I live in when I go home in the spring, so that you can run over parts we have not visited and tell us what is there. Will you like doing that?

HAKI Ay, sir.

LEIF The place I come from is a long way from here. We shall go there in a ship.

HAKI Ay.

HAEKIA Will they laugh at us there?

LEIF No. Why should they?

HAKI The people in this town make fun of us because we do not understand their ways, and they laugh at our clothes. We do not like this place. When first we came to Norway we were on a farm to herd the sheep. We were happy there. Are there farms in your country?

91

LEIF We all live on farms in my country; there are no towns. In my country nobody will laugh at you. Do you come with me willingly?

HAKI Ay, sir.

HAEKIA They say you are a kind master. We would like that fine.

LEIF All right. I see that town life doesn't suit you two. I will ask King Olaf if you may go back onto the farm till it is time for us to start.

[FADE TO:

The Quayside

(*The camera opens on a field of blue and white hepatica in the sun to show the lapse of time; it lifts and shows* LEIF's *ship at the quayside; the ship is fully loaded and about to leave. She is deeply loaded with a cargo of timber and iron goods, so that the space left for the crew is small.* HAKI *and* HAEKI *are on board, standing very close together and staring with wonder at everything they see; near them is the priest, who has clearly taken the two* SCOTS *under his care.*)

(*On the quay there is a crowd of men to see them off.* LEIF *is there, talking to* KING OLAF.)

LEIF We are ready to go now, sir. With this fair wind we shall be over the horizon before noon, even with all this cargo you have given us.

KING OLAF Go then, with my goodwill and with the blessing of God. Remember all that I have told you. Push on and find new countries to the southwards of your Greenland if you can; I don't think you'll do much good where you are. Take my greetings to your father, and tell him that he's not an outlaw any longer. Let the good priest do his good work amongst your people, and let him teach them writing. Send a written letter to me each year by the ship.

LEIF Sir, I will do all these things.

(*He bows to the* KING *and goes down to the ship. Shot of the ship leaving land.*)

[DISSOLVE TO:

The Ship at Sea

(*The ship is sailing in sunshine with a fair wind. In the cramped space on board the* PRIEST *is seated with a cross in his hand; he is talking earnestly to* HAKI *and* HAEKIA *who are listening to him intently. In the background members of the crew are looking on curiously. This conversion scene requires no dialogue; it should be possible to make it clear that the* PRIEST *is starting off upon the easiest people in the ship, the humblest people. In a following shot* HAKI *and* HAEKIA *may be seen crouched together like children, very intent on private business of their own;* HAKI *is whittling a little wooden cross. In later scenes throughout the film they may be seen wearing these little crosses slung round their necks by a rawhide thong.*)

(*In all these ship scenes* LEIF *and* TYRKER *should be shown working at the steering oar, preoccupied with the sailing of the ship. The life of the ship goes on at their feet unnoticed.*)

[DISSOLVE TO:

The Classroom

(CALLENDER *is at the map, indicating.*)

CALLENDER They probably went direct from Norway to Greenland in the early summer of that year—like this. The saga does not say that they put in to any port between. They had the notch for Greenland carved upon their thwart, of course, so they probably got straight onto their latitude as soon as they could and went all the way with a fair easterly wind. So they got back to Ericsfirth in Greenland.

[DISSOLVE TO:

The Ship at Ericsfirth

(*This is an evening scene. In a short opening shot the ship is seen sailing into the fiord. She beaches at Brattahlid; there is a crowd on the shore to meet them headed by* ERIC, *now an old man. As the ship grounds or comes to a quay—whichever is most suitable—all these people come on board; the ship is crowded with wives greeting husbands, children, etc. In this noisy confusion the* PRIEST *stands apart with the two* SCOTS *by him; they are all wearing crosses.*)

(LEIF *shows his father the cargo of the ship.*)

LEIF They gave us everything I asked for, Father; they were terribly good to us. I had to stay the winter, but I'm glad I did; I learned a lot about shipbuilding and I had some long talks with the King. All this timber is in twenty-foot lengths. These are the iron nails. This case has thirty iron ploughshares in it, already made up for us, Father; we shall not have to forge them up ourselves. This is the brass, and they gave us these copper sheets for cooking vessels, too. I have so much to tell you it will take all winter.

ERIC   (*Very pleased, stroking the wood*) Such beautiful, straight pieces! I had almost forgotten that there was wood like this in the world. (*Turns to* BJARNI, *who is near*) Bjarni, look at all this beautiful straight wood that Leif has brought from Norway. Pity you didn't do as well.

BJARNI   (*Resentful*) Nobody ever told me that you needed wood. I could have brought you better wood than this, but nobody ever tells me anything.

LEIF   What's all this about?

ERIC   When Bjarni was on his way here from Iceland he got over to the west a bit and saw another land on which there were tall trees. And if you please, he came here with an empty ship!

BJARNI   Well, how was I to know you wanted wood? Every decent country has a lot of wood. You can't build ships without it.

(ERIC *turns from him in disgust and examines the other materials.*)

LEIF   (*Keenly*) Where was this country, Bjarni? Was it south from here?

BJARNI   I did not come direct. Yes, I suppose the place with the timber would have been about southwest from here, or maybe further south than that.

LEIF   What sort of country was it, Bjarni? Was it beautiful?

BJARNI   I don't know about that. I didn't go too near it, because I didn't know the coast.

LEIF   Was it fertile country? Was there pasture on it, and streams of water?

95

BJARNI I suppose there might have been. I didn't notice specially.

LEIF Was there any snow?

BJARNI Oh, no, there wasn't any snow. It was quite warm.

LEIF Would flowers grow there, and fruit?

BJARNI You do ask a lot of fool questions. I don't go for fruit much, myself. I like meat, or fish.

LEIF But would fruit grow there—would it ripen in the summer?

BJARNI It was pretty hot the day that we were there.

(*It is sunset now.* LEIF *turns and looks towards the west, where the sunset colours glow and fade across the sky. He is standing at the prow of the ship by the carved dragon of the figurehead, silhouetted against the sunset.*)

(THORGUNNA'S *voice is heard.*)

THORGUNNA Past the horizon and beyond those rosy clouds there lies the Happy Land, which this man called Hy Breasail. No thief, no robber, and no enemy pursues one there; there is no violence, and no winter snow. In that place it is always spring. No flower or lily is wanting, no rose or violet but you will find them there. There apple trees bear flowers and fruit on the same branch, all the year round. There young men live in quiet happiness with their girls; there is no old age, and no sickness and no sorrow there. All is full of joy . . .

(*The fade comes slowly on the sunset scene, with* LEIF *silhouetted against the sky.*)

[FADE TO:

Hall of Eric's Farmhouse

(*This is a fairly large room, not so big as the hall of the King in the Hebrides, but big enough to contain most of the characters in Greenland named so far in the story. ERIC's wife, THORHILD, is seated at the head of a long table, with ERIC beside her. It is a feast scene at which all the characters are seated. There is a large fire, and the room is lit by torches. Everybody is drinking heavily.*)

(ERIC's *wife is a stern-faced woman who holds great authority in the community.* ERIC *is shown as a good-humoured, stout man, still fairly vigorous but growing old and much addicted to drink, the fireside, and a quiet life.*)

BJARNI   I've told you all I know. We saw the place, and there was wood on it. Lots of countries have woods on them—all decent countries do. I don't know why you are all so excited about it.

LEIF   We can always use more wood.

BJARNI   Well, I'll sail to Norway and get you some more. I'd like to go to Norway, anyway.

LEIF   This other place is closer.

BJARNI   You're just reckless. You might run into all sorts of trouble, going off to a new place you don't know anything about. You'll end up by getting yourself bewitched and turned into a rabbit or a deer. I've heard of that.

ERIC   That's right—Wotan did that to Sigurd. If anybody's going to those places he should make blood sacrifice to Wotan first.

THORHILD   Be quiet, you old pagan. How many times have I got to tell you that we will not have that sort of talk? We are all good Christians here. What will the good priest think?

97

(*The* PRIEST *makes a deprecating gesture of tolerance.*)

ERIC   Speak for yourself, woman. I'm not a good Christian, I don't want to be a good Christian, and I'm not going to be a good Christian, and that's all about it. I think a voyage to the land that Bjarni saw to get a cargo of that wood would be a good thing. We've used half of the stuff Leif brought back from Norway already. But if I have anything to do with it there'll be blood sacrifice before we start. It's just tempting Wotan to show what he can do, to start without a sacrifice.

THORHILD   Quiet, man. To say such things before the priest!

ERIC   Priest! He's an impostor, that's what he is. He breaks up marriages, that's what he does. Breaks up a man's happy marriage. (*He weeps a little.*)

THORHILD   If I've told you once I've told you twenty times. I'll sleep with you again when you become a Christian and not before. It's not lawful for a Christian to be married to a pagan, you old reprobate.

ERIC   Well, what did you want to go and become Christian for? I tell you, the man just spends his time breaking up marriages, happy, happy marriages. If I was ten years younger I'd break him up.

THORHILD   (*Fiercely*) Peace!

A MAN   (*Coughing*) About this journey for the wood that we were talking about. I think we ought to go next summer. We want a lot of wood.

SECOND MAN   Ay. Eric, let's have an expedition next year to the place that Bjarni saw, and get a cargo of that wood.

SEVERAL MEN   Ay, let's do that, Eric.

ERIC   Bjarni, will you take an expedition to the country?

BJARNI Well, I don't know. There aren't any people there. I'd rather go to Norway. It's a bit further, but I like being at sea. You can have a good time in Norway.

FIRST MAN What's all this stuff about Bjarni? We don't want to go with Bjarni and spend all our time at sea and never get on shore at all. Eric's our leader.

SEVERAL MEN Ay. Eric must lead us.

ERIC Me?

SECOND MAN Ay. You can sail the ship all right. We won't go unless you lead us.

ERIC Well now, boys, this wants a bit of thinking over. I've got a lot to do next summer.

THORHILD You had nothing to do last summer except lean on the fence rail and chew a straw, and make eyes at the serving girls. You did enough of that, and you didn't stop at making eyes, either. You made other things besides.

ERIC (*Loftily*) You don't want to pay any attention to her.

THIRD MAN (*Craftily*) Lady, if Eric led this expedition he couldn't get any more girls into trouble.

THORHILD That's very true. Eric shall lead the expedition to the land that Bjarni saw. (*Lifts her mug*) Skaal.

ALL THE MEN *Skaal!*

ERIC (*Grumbling*) I never said I'd go.

THORHILD *I* did.

[FADE TO:

99

Farmyard at Brattahlid

(HAKI *and* HAEKIA *are working at a haystack getting hay for animals; it is a winter scene and there is snow on the ground.* TYRKER *comes up and touches* HAKI *on the shoulder.*)

TYRKER   Your lord Leif wants you in the hall.

[DISSOLVE TO:

Hall of the Farmhouse

(LEIF *is seated informally on the dais, on a bed or a heap of furs.* TYRKER *comes in, followed by* HAKI. TYRKER *goes up on to the dais and stands behind* LEIF; HAKI *stands before him on the lower part of the floor.*)

LEIF   Haki, have you heard the story that Bjarni saw a new country to the south and west from here, where there were tall trees?

HAKI   Ay, Lord.

LEIF   Well, Bjarni didn't even land! He might quite well have brought us back a cargo of that lumber, and he didn't! I never heard anything like it!

HAKI   With big trees we could build a new cowhouse.

LEIF   That's right. We can build proper houses like we saw in Norway if we get the timber for the roofs. We might even have a go at building ships. Next summer we are going in a ship to find the land that Bjarni saw, to get a cargo of that lumber.

HAKI   Lord, how will you ever find that place again? There are no landmarks on the sea.

LEIF   We have bought Bjarni's ship. The ship will know the way back to the lumber, because it has been there before.

HAKI (*In awe*) The dragon on the ship will know the way. (*Crosses himself*)

LEIF (*Smiling*) Yes, the dragon on the ship will know where the wood is. Now, look here, Haki. I want you and Haekia to come with me. If there are new lands to be found I must send word back to the King, and you can run across the land and tell me what it is like.

HAKI We can do that, Lord.

LEIF I want you to think about this for a day or so, and talk it over with Haekia. This journey will be difficult and dangerous; I do not even know where we are going. Every one coming with me must come willingly; I will not order any one to come upon a trip like this. Do you understand me?

HAKI (*Puzzled*) No, Lord.

LEIF Well, I say this. You and Haekia are a pair; I will not take one of you alone. If you two want to stay behind here, you may do so. But if you come with me, and if you do good work, then when we get back you shall be free people. I will set you free, and I will give you land to farm for yourselves, and beasts to start you off. I will do this for you if you come with me, but you must talk to Haekia first.

HAKI Lord, we would have come with you anyway, but for these gifts we would follow you through hell.

(TYRKER *stoops and whispers something to* LEIF; *he nods.*)

LEIF There is another thing. I will not have any unattached girl in the ship; when men are far from their wives they will quarrel over her, and fight. Are you and Haekia lovers? Do you sleep with her?

HAKI Lord, she does not think about such things yet. Besides, she sleeps with the women.

101

(LEIF *throws back his head and laughs uproariously, rocking on his seat. Behind him* TYRKER *stands, smiling gently.* HAKI *is utterly nonplussed; he does not understand in the least what* LEIF *is laughing about.*)

LEIF   You two will be the death of me. So. Before we sail Haekia must be betrothed to you, and I shall be the witness. If anybody takes a fancy to her then he'll have to face a fight with me, and I shall kill him, according to our laws. In that way I can keep my crew in order.

HAKI   (*Obediently*) Ay, Lord.

LEIF   Go and have a talk with Haekia now. Come back to-morrow and tell me whether you two want to come along with me or to stay here as slaves.

[DISSOLVE TO:

The Farmyard

(HAKI *and* HAEKIA *are talking in a sheltered corner by the hayrick.*)

HAKI   If we go with him and if we please him with our running, he will make us free, and he will give us our own land to farm, and cows of our own. We should be free people then, like everybody else. (*He glances at her; the camera should dwell on her short hair and her white garment.*) You would be able to let your hair grow long, and wear dark clothes and ornaments, like other free women.

HAEKIA   All this is very good, Haki. Of course we will go. When is he going to start?

HAKI   (*Awkwardly*) There's just one thing. If we go, Leif says that you must be betrothed to me, in case the men come after you and fight with each other. (*He hesitates.*) This is for order in the ship. We can always break the betrothal when we get back here, if you don't want to marry.

HAEKIA (*Smiling*) I don't want to marry anybody yet, Haki. But we are the same people, and we think the same way, and we laugh at the same things. I would rather marry you than anybody else when the time comes.

HAKI (*Thoughtfully*) Perhaps if we please him Leif will give us land right away on the outskirts of the settlement, where we can live in our own way.

HAEKIA (*Earnestly*) That would be very, very good.

[DISSOLVE TO:

The Beach

(BJARNI's *ship is being loaded for the voyage. This should be a spring scene; there should be no snow. It is a scene of great activity, with many men carrying the stores and gear on board under the direction of* LEIF.)

(HAKI *and* HAEKIA *come out of the crowd and stand looking up at the carved dragon on the bow of the ship; this is a very fierce dragon.* HAEKIA *crosses herself. In the background,* LEIF *sees them and stops whatever he is doing.*)

LEIF You two Scots, come over here! (*They go to him; he stands erect and shouts.*) Hold everything a minute, men, and listen to this. A betrothal!

(*Around them the work stops; men lay down their burdens and look at* LEIF *curiously. He turns to the* SCOTS.)

103

—Take her hand, Haki. Do you know what to say?

HAKI   No, Lord.

LEIF   Well, say this after me, and shout it out so that every one can hear you. 'I name Leif Ericsson as witness that you, Haekia, betroth yourself to me, Haki, in a lawful betrothal, with hand-shaking and with no fraud or tricks.'

HAKI   I name Leif Ericsson as witness that you, Haekia, betroth yourself to me, Haki, in a lawful betrothal, with handshaking, and with no fraud or tricks.

(*There is an interested murmur from the crowd.*)

LEIF   Now listen to me, all of you. This woman belongs to this man, and I am witness to the lawful betrothal. I do this by the order of our King in Norway, who gave me these two slaves. If anybody takes a fancy to the girl, he'll have to deal with me. Now get on with your work, all the lot of you.

(*There is a laugh, and the men resume their work.*)

[DISSOLVE TO:

Eric's Farmyard

(*There is a great bustle of preparation for the start of the expedition; there is a succession of men carrying burdens from the house down a track towards the beach.*)

(*Eric is seen about to mount upon a very small horse or pony to ride down to the beach. A Shetland pony might do; the effect must be a very large man on a very small horse. Thor-hild is with him.*)

THORHILD   Get on now, and get along down to the beach, or they'll go without you.

ERIC (*Hopefully*) Will they?

THORHILD If you don't get going I shall tell them all that Eric the Red, the great leader, is afraid to go.

ERIC Peace, woman.

THORHILD Well, get on and go. I don't know what you want to ride for, anyway. Can't you walk that far? You could if there was a pretty girl down on the beach.

ERIC Hold your tongue. There is a proper way to do things, and it's dignified for the leader to ride a horse down to his ship. They do that in Norway.

THORHILD All right, get on and go.

ERIC Did you say something about a pretty girl down there?

THORHILD Dozens of them. Now, get on.

(*She helps him into the saddle and he rides off down the track, with* THORHILD *walking beside him.*)

[DISSOLVE TO:

The Beach Head

(ERIC *appears riding his pony on the track, with* THORHILD *walking beside him.*)

(*The pony shies at something and pecks a little.* ERIC *slides off onto the ground and lies there moaning. It is a palpably faked accident. People come running up in concern.*)

THORHILD Well, what's the matter now?

ERIC (*Sitting on the ground*) I've broken my ankle.

THORHILD Nonsense.

(*A crowd gathers round, much concerned. Two very beauti-ful girls help* ERIC *to his feet; he stands holding one foot off the ground, with an arm round the shoulders of each lovely girl.*)

(*He stands erect. He is taller than everybody, and in spite of his slightly farcical character and the girls supporting him, there should be dignity in him at this moment.*)

ERIC Hear this, everybody. This is an omen. I have found new lands in my time, but it is quite clear that I am not destined to find any more. I'm getting an old man now, and I must stay at home. I name my son Leif to lead the expedition in my place.

LEIF Father, won't you come?

ERIC You must go in my place. This accident has been a warning to us all; if I lead you we shall all meet with a disaster. You, Leif, are to lead this expedition in my place.

SEVERAL MEN Leif! Leif the Lucky is going to lead us, and we shall do well. Leif the Lucky!

(ERIC *stands watching the beach, supported by the girls.*)

THORHILD You'll meet with a disaster all right. Wait till I get you home!

⌈ CUT TO:

The Beach—Later

(*The ship is setting off upon her voyage, drawing away from the beach.* LEIF *is at the steering oar, with* TYRKER *beside him.* HAKI *and* HAEKIA *are in the well of the ship. She is manned by about fifteen men; she carries a small boat on board. There*

is also a fully grown bullock on board, which was taken as a
draught animal to pull tree trunks down to the ship.)

(On shore, a little group of people stand waving good-bye,
ERIC *and* BJARNI *amongst them, and the* PRIEST.*)*

[DISSOLVE TO:

The Classroom

CALLENDER It wasn't much of a send-off for people who were
going to make history. But that's the way things happen. They
went out to get lumber to build cowhouses, and they found
America. (*He turns to the map.*) They landed first in Labrador
across the Davis Strait—here. They had to go there first because
that was the way that Bjarni came to Greenland, and they followed his course back to find the wood.

[DISSOLVE TO:

Labrador Fiord

(The ship is sailing into a Labrador fiord. There are no trees,
and the ground is barren, covered with large slabs of stone,
partly snow covered. It is a very desolate scene. The ship
anchors, and they put a boat over the side.)

[DISSOLVE TO:

Labrador Beach

(The boat pulls in and grounds upon the beach. LEIF *and*

TYRKER get out; other men stay in the boat. LEIF and TYRKER walk a little way from the boat to the head of the beach and stand looking out over the bleak country.)

LEIF This is probably the place that Bjarni came to last. I never saw a worse country. It's no good to us.

TYRKER Ice, and snow, and rocks—we've got all those at home.

LEIF I don't see any point in staying here. We'll get to sea again, and go on down the coast.

TYRKER Lord, though this land is useless, yet it ought to have a name.

LEIF All right. What shall we call it?

TYRKER I don't know. You think of something. You're the Chief.

LEIF (*Looking round*) Well, I don't know. There's nothing decent to call it after—the wretched place is all stones. We'd better call it Stoneland.

TYRKER That's as good as anything.

LEIF Let's see, now. Bjarni sailed north along the coast to get to this place, didn't he?

TYRKER Yes. If we sail south for a few days from here, we ought to come to the place where he saw the woods.

LEIF All right. Let's get going.

(*They get back into the boat, which rows out to the ship. The ship takes the boat on board, weighs anchor, and leaves the fiord.*)

(*A shot of the ship sailing down a rocky coast. There may be small lumps of ice in the sea, and a grey sky.*)

(*Up to this point the film has been a picture of a bleak life* of hardships, of men struggling to exist and make a living against a background of ice and snow, rough grey seas, and barren, windswept, stony land. But from this point onwards the scenes must grow sunnier and more beautiful as they get further south. There are to be no more rough seas and ice. The whole montage should be designed to show them entering into a softer and more gracious land than any they had known before. This should not be a sudden change but should grow, culminating in the final scenes in the district of Plymouth, Mass., at midsummer.)

[DISSOLVE TO:

The Ship—Dawn Scene

(*The light grows slowly, and the ship is seen to be cruising off the wooded coast that* BJARNI *visited before.* LEIF *and* TYRKER *are at the steering oar; in the body of the ship every one is looking at the land.*)

TYRKER Lord, this must be the place that Bjarni saw. We were nearly on the latitude at our noon sight yesterday, and we sailed slowly all the night. I think this is the place, all right.

LEIF I think so, too. We will go in here and beach the ship upon those sands. (*Shouts*) Out bow oars, men; I'm going to put her up into the wind to lower sail. Stand by the vangs, and heave in on the lee sheet. Get your halliard cleared away, and be ready for it.

(*The ship comes up into the wind and the sail is lowered. The rest of the oars are put out, and she begins to row into the beach.*)

[DISSOLVE TO:

The Beach

(*The ship strands on the beach; men jump out into the shallow water and carry anchors and cables on shore. LEIF follows them.*)

(*A shot of LEIF standing with HAKI and HAEKIA on the head of the beach.*)

LEIF You two. Go up onto that hill there quickly. Look carefully what lies beyond it. Then make a sweep round there— (*points*)—and come back here within two hours. Tell me if you see any signs of men in this place. If you see men, do not go near them; run back quickly here and tell me.

(*The SCOTS set off running.*)

(*A shot of the SCOTS standing together on the hilltop, looking out over a thickly wooded country.*)

(*A shot of the SCOTS running through a forest glade. HAEKIA stops for a moment beside a stream to pick a flower, and then runs on.*)

[DISSOLVE TO:

Camp on the Beach

(*The ship is high and dry, and the Norsemen have made a fire and a rudimentary camp at the head of the beach. The SCOTS come running into camp, and go to LEIF.*)

LEIF Well, what did you see?

HAKI Lord, we have seen no signs of any men in this place. There is much forest here; from the hilltop you can only see the tops of trees, right over to the far horizon. We saw many deer.

There is a good stream of fresh water running to the sea beyond that point.

LEIF   Good.

HAEKIA   We found flowers, Lord. (*She shows them;* LEIF *and* TYRKER *examine them curiously.*)

LEIF   I have never seen flowers like these before. So big, and such bright colours!

TYRKER   I remember seeing flowers as big and bright as these when I was a small boy in Germany. I have never seen them in these northern countries.

HAEKIA   They are lovely. May I keep them, Lord?

LEIF   Yes, if you want them.

[DISSOLVE TO:

The Camp—Later

(*The men have had a meal and are sitting round the fire after it.* LEIF *is standing with* TYRKER *by his side; he is addressing them.*)

LEIF   Well, men, we've found the timber that we came to get. We could load up now and get away straight back to Greenland. But now we're here, I think it would be a pity not to sail around a bit and find out what this place is like. It looks to me to be a better country than our own. I know my father will be very much interested in it. Some of us might want to come here someday and make a settlement.

A MAN   What are you going to call this place?

LEIF Well, I don't know. We don't know very much about it yet, except that it's all woods. Suppose we call it Woodland?

MAN Woodland. That's a good name for it.

LEIF What do you men say about going on a bit, and seeing what else we can find? It's early in the summer to go home.

A MAN Your father's order was that we should bring back wood.

LEIF We can get the wood when we come back past here in a month's time, on our way home. It was the King's order that we should seek new lands towards the west and south, and that is what I mean to do, if you will follow me.

A MAN (*Laughing*) All right. Have it your own way.

[DISSOLVE TO:

The Ship

(*The ship is seen sailing past wooded, rocky coasts in fine, calm weather.*)

(*A shot of the ship on an open sea crossing.*)

[DISSOLVE TO:

The Classroom

CALLENDER They turned the corner of the land at Cape Race, here (*indicates on the map*), and then cut over to the coast of Nova Scotia, sailing south and west. And each day as they sailed the weather grew finer, and the sea grew calmer, and the sun grew stronger. From Nova Scotia, here, they sailed on, here, across the sea until they hit the tip of Cape Cod, here. And they were very much amazed.

$\bigl[$ DISSOLVE TO:

The Ship

(*She is off the north tip of Cape Cod and all the crew are staring at the beach, which extends unbroken to the southeast as far as they can see. This beach is quite even and regular and exactly the same in appearance for about forty miles, unbroken by any reef or promontory. It must be almost unique in the world for its regularity. Beyond it the land is low-lying.*)

TYRKER Lord, here is yet another land, and this one is all beach. There is no end to the new places we have seen.

LEIF We'll land and have a look at it as soon as we can, but I'm not going to put a boat on shore through that surf. We'll follow the beach southwards till we find an opening.

(*The ship turns and begins to coast along the beach, perhaps a quarter of a mile offshore.*)

$\bigl[$ DISSOLVE TO:

The Ship—Later

(*The ship is still sailing down this endless beach.*)

TYRKER Lord, there is no beach in the world like this. We've been sailing along it now for over six hours, and it's been exactly the same all the way. You just can't tell the difference between any two parts of it.

LEIF I know. It's a great wonder.

TYRKER So strange a place as this ought to have a name. It is a

landmark that men coming from the sea will recognize. What shall
we call it, Lord?

LEIF Well, I don't know. It's a great wonder, and that's all about
it. We'd better call it Wonderstrands.

TYRKER (*Calling out*) Listen to this, everybody. This long beach
that we have sailed along all day is to be called Wonderstrands.

(*There is a murmur of assent.*)

⌈ DISSOLVE TO:

The Island

(*This is an evening scene. The ship is coming in to beach on
a low, sandy island covered with trees, lying half a mile or so
off the long beach of Wonderstrands. This island, Nauset
Island, has now disappeared entirely by erosion; it used to lie
off the beach opposite Orleans. It is a warm, sunny evening,
nearly sunset; the island is a fairyland, covered with trees and
flowers.*)

⌈ DISSOLVE TO:

The Beach

(*The ship is stranded on the beach, and the men are spread-
ing out along the foreshore and the beach head. It is sunset
and most beautiful, as beautiful as can be contrived. The men
are moving quietly, looking around them in wonder and in
awe at such a lovely place.*)

(*Presently one of them stoops to pick a flower. His finger*

114

strikes something sticky on a leaf; he licks it and exclaims. Presently several of the men are picking leaves and licking them.)

A MAN Lord, there is honey on the leaves in this island.

(Leif *and* Tyrker *pick leaves and try them.*)

TYRKER (*In awe*) Lord, this is honey dew. In my country, in the old stories that old people tell around the fireside in the winter, they say that in the Happy Land honey falls like dew from heaven in the night.

LEIF (*Thoughtfully*) The Happy Land . . .

(*He looks around. Through a thin screen of a few trees he sees the sunset, bright and rosy in the west. Between the trees he sees* Haki *walking with* Haekia; *they are laughing together at some private joke of their own. This scene must be as beautiful as can be contrived.*)

LEIF (*Quietly*) I heard once of the Happy Land, which some men call Hy Breasail. No thief, no robber, and no enemy pursues one there; there is no violence, and no winter snow. In that place it is always spring. No flower or lily is wanting, no rose or violet but you will find them there.

(*During this speech the camera should pick up these features one by one, verifying them visually.*)

—There apple trees bear flowers and fruit on the same branch, all the year round. There young men live in quiet happiness with their girls (*the camera picks up* Haki *and* Haekia, *engrossed in each other*); there is no old age and no sickness and no sorrow there. All is full of joy.

TYRKER (*Uneasily*) Lord, do you think that this place is Hy Breasail?

LEIF (*Rousing*) I don't know. I know only this; it is so beautiful that it might well be we have found the Happy Land. I will not spend the night here; we may be bewitched. We will anchor off shore for the night and sleep in the ship.

[DISSOLVE TO:

The Anchorage

(*It is a late evening scene, almost night. The ship is anchored off the beach; it is cloudless, and dead calm. The island lies silhouetted against the faint remnants of the sunset, very beautiful. In the ship the dim forms of men are seen staring at the beauty of the scene, silent and in wonder.*)

[FADE TO:

The Classroom

CALLENDER Next morning they set sail again towards the south. (*Indicates on the map.*) They turned the corner of the land by Chatham, here, and sailed along the south shore of Cape Cod into Nantucket Sound. And on the south shore of the Cape they landed, setting foot for the first time on the American continent.

[DISSOLVE TO:

The Landing

(*For the location of this landing, which the saga and historical analysis define only as somewhere on the south coast of*

Cape Cod, I suggest that they enter Osterville Harbour and proceed right up into the little land-locked, tree-enclosed pool (unnamed) half a mile south of Marstons Mills (Map Reference, U. S. Geological Survey, Barnstable, Mass., quadrangle). Alternatively a suitable site could be found two miles west, in Poponesset Bay.)

(The ship enters a wooded creek or bay. She approaches a beach and strands; the men get out of her and make her fast with anchors and ropes.)

[DISSOLVE TO:

Camp at the Beach Head

(A camp has been made and tents pitched as at the Hebrides, because the Norsemen mean to stay here for several days. LEIF and TYRKER are talking to HAKI and HAEKIA.)

LEIF Well, we've found the wood, Haki; the wood we need at home for our cowhouses. I don't think we can go on any further; these new lands may go on and on to the end of the world. We're going to camp here and cut and trim these trees, enough to load the ship. Then we will turn for home.

HAKI Ay, Lord.

LEIF Well now, about you two. We shall be staying here for several days. To-morrow morning at dawn, I want you to set off to run towards the west to find out what sort of a country this is. You can be away for three days. To-morrow you will run straight inland, and part of the next day, and on the third day you will come back by a different way so that you can give me an account of as much of the country as can be seen in the time. Do you understand what I want to know?

HAKI Lord, we understand very well. You want to know the sort of country, whether it is marsh or field or forest or mountain; you want to know the animals and birds, and whether there are signs of men. You want to know the rivers and the lakes, and the flowers and the fruits that we find by the way. All these things we will notice; on the evening of the third day you shall have our story.

LEIF Good. Will you take food with you?

HAKI Lord, we do not like to carry burdens; we cannot travel quickly unless we go light. We will take tinder to make fire with, and a flint and steel. We will eat before we go.

TYRKER (*Giving* HAEKIA *a pouch*) Here is some tinder. There's not much there; I'll get you some more before you go.

LEIF (*Unbuckling a belt with a sheath knife from his waist*) Take this knife. It's a good one, I got it in Norway. Don't lose it.

HAKI Lord, I will bring it safely back to you three days from now.

[DISSOLVE TO:

The Camp—Dawn Scene

(*Every one is asleep except one sentry on watch, silhouetted against the sky.* HAKI *and* HAEKIA *are sleeping by the fire;* HAEKIA *wakes and shakes* HAKI. *They get up from their sleeping bags. There is a litter of food and half-gnawed bones on a platter, the remains of their evening meal; they eat a little of this. Then they speak to the sentry, and set off running from the camp in the grey light of dawn. They run steadily, not very fast, for they have a long way to go. They are lost to sight among the trees.*)

118

[DISSOLVE TO:

The Pond

(*They are running together in full daylight round the shore of a lake amongst fir trees, with white, sandy beaches. Snake Pond, near Forest Dale, is suitable.*)

HAEKIA (*Pointing*) Be careful how you go. Haki; there are serpents here. Don't go and tread on one.

HAKI Remember to tell Leif. We saw snakes by the pond.

(*They run on.*)

[DISSOLVE TO:

The Hilltop

(*They are standing for a moment, panting a little, looking westwards.*)

HAKI I believe this land that we are standing on is a cape. There is the sea (*points*)—and there (*points the other way*) is the sea again.

HAEKIA There is land everywhere to the west, over there, right up to those blue hills on the horizon. This is a very big country, Haki. We must go westwards.

HAKI I think there is a bridge of land for us to go by. I do not think this is an island; I think there are two bays, one to the north and one to the south, that do not quite meet.

HAEKIA (*Pointing*) There is a buzzard. Look, Haki, there are several of them, over the sea there. Remember to tell Leif.

HAKI I will mind that. There are buzzards over the south bay.

[DISSOLVE TO:

The Journey

(*This journey of exploration should be told very largely without dialogue. The photography must be as beautiful as can be managed, the whole point lying in the contrast with the hardships and bleak lands of the early part of the film.*)

(*A shot of the two* SCOTS *running steadily inland, leaving the sea behind them. It may be convenient to make this an estuary scene, and show them striking off into beautiful country away from the dwindling river.*)

(*Dissolve to a late afternoon scene. They are walking now, hand-in-hand, still going on towards the west, but more slowly because they find so much to look at and to wonder at. A succession of shots should show them walking beneath tall forest trees, in meadows beside streams, over an open heath. A shot should show* HAEKIA *stooping to pick berries.*)

HAEKIA Look, Haki—these are cranberries!

HAKI They are so big!

(*Dissolve to another shot or two to show them wandering on, picking various berries and fruits, and exclaiming at the birds and animals that they see.*)

HAKI There is so much to tell Leif about this country that we shall never be finished.

HAEKIA It is the best country we have ever seen, Haki. It is better than Greenland, better than Norway, better even than Scotland.

HAKI There is no limit to the number of cows a farmer could keep here. There is grass for all the cows and sheep in the world.

HAEKIA (*Happily*) It is very good to be here, Haki. The land is beautiful, and it is good to be alone together and away from the Norsemen for a bit.

HAKI I know. Leif is kind and just, but we have our ways aı they have theirs, and the two are different.

(*Dissolve to a shot of a little deer in a glade. The two* SCOTS *see it, nudge each other, and pick up pebbles from a brook. They stalk it from two directions. Both throw their stones at it at the same moment and both hit it on the head; it falls down and they run up to despatch it with the knife.*)

(*Dissolve to a shot of* HAKI *carrying it over his shoulders, with* HAEKIA *at his side; they are very pleased with themselves.*)

(*Dissolve to a late evening shot of their camp. They have made a fire and a windbreak and a bed of fir twigs; they have cooked a good part of the deer on wooden skewers, and they are eating it. They have made themselves very comfortable.*)

(*Dissolve to a shot of them asleep together on the bed, the fire is dying down. It is a fine, starry night.*)

[FADE TO:

(*A morning scene; they are running through the woods together.*)

(*A midday scene. They are walking hand-in-hand by a river. They see a scarlet tanager and are amazed at it; they try to catch it, laughing.*)

(*An old Indian camp site, long deserted. The* SCOTS *are examining it warily, turning over the ashes and examining chopped sticks.*)

121

(A scene of them swimming across a river, side by side. They get out, shake themselves like dogs, and go on.)

(An evening scene. They have made a campfire by the sea beneath cedar (or similar) trees, very beautiful. A shot of them asleep together.)

(A morning scene. They are running along a beach on their way back to the cape.)

$$\left[\text{ DISSOLVE TO:} \right.$$

Leif's Camp

(An evening scene. There are many trees felled and a great litter of chips and brushwood. The ship is seen partly loaded with trimmed trunks; the whole atmosphere is now that of a lumber camp, for this is the whole object of the journey. The bullock is seen at work, dragging the felled timber of trees towards the ship. LEIF is sitting before his tent eating his supper; TYRKER comes to him.)

TYRKER   Lord, the Scots are coming in.

(LEIF gets up from the fire and walks with TYRKER to the edge of the camp. In the distance the SCOTS are seen running towards them through a glade; they come up to LEIF. They are panting a little, but they are not unduly distressed. HAKI is carrying a few ears of wild wheat, and HAEKIA has a couple of bunches of small grapes.)

LEIF   So—you are back. Did you see any signs of men?

HAKI   Lord, there are men in this country, but we did not see them. We found traces of their fire, but they were old.

TYRKER   Is the land good?

122

HAKI Lord, we have so much to tell you it will take all night. This is a good country, better than Norway or my own land, better than Greenland. There are animals and flowers and fruit of every sort. All the cattle in the world could pasture here, and there is food for every one. It is the best land in the world.

LEIF So. What have you got there?

HAKI Lord, we brought this grain for you to see. It is wheat. We found it growing wild, and that is a great wonder.

LEIF (*Examining the ears*) It is not the wheat we use for bread, but it is a grain very like it. I should think you might be able to make bread of this.

HAEKIA (*Shyly, offering her grapes*) Lord, we found these berries and all the birds were eating them, and so we ate them too. They were very good.

(*She hands* LEIF *the grapes, and then moves a little closer to* HAKI; *their hands meet down by their side.* LEIF *glances at them; clearly they are very much in love. He laughs.*)

LEIF Did you enjoy your journey?
(HAEKIA *smiles shyly, and says nothing.*)

HAKI Lord, when we are old and grey and ill, and near to death, we shall still be thinking about this fine journey we have made.

LEIF (*Smiling*) So. Do you two want to be married now?

(HAKI *looks at* HAEKIA; *they smile together.*)

HAKI Lord, we would like that fine.

LEIF I will marry you in the morning—remind me after breakfast, and I'll get the men together. It's all right for slaves to go on as you have been doing, but free people should be married, especially if they are Christians, as you are. You have done very well, you two. You shall be free people when we get back home, living on your own farm with cattle of your own.

123

(*The* Scots *are very pleased.* Tyrker, *who has been examining the grapes, breaks in.*)

TYRKER Lord, I know these fruits quite well. They grow in Germany, where I was born. They are called grapes. You make wine out of them.

LEIF (*Tasting one*) Oh, these are grapes, are they? I have heard of grapes, but I have never seen them before. I have drunk wine; it's a very good drink.

TYRKER Lord, if we can get some more of them I will make wine for you, as my people do at home.

LEIF So. Then we will call this good new country Vinland, Vinland the Good.

TYRKER (*Turning to the men and shouting*) Listen to me, everybody—pay attention. My lord says that we will call this good new country Vinland, Vinland the Good.

(*There is a murmur of assent from the men. Faintly at first the school bell is heard ringing for the end of the lesson; it grows in crescendo as the beach and camp scene slowly fades.*)

[FADE TO:

The Classroom

(*The bell is still tolling.*)

CALLENDER Well, that's all that we've got time for in this lesson. The Norsemen never settled in their Vinland though they made a lot of journeys to it. They could not fight the Indians with the small numbers they could land; each time they tried to

124

make a settlement the Indians came down on them and beat them in a battle. It wasn't until five hundred years later, when men came with the new weapons they called guns, that Europeans settled in America. Some of them, right down in the south, were certain they had found Hy Breasail, by the way, which you would call Brazil.

BOY ONE Brazil!

CALLENDER And now I'm going to say just one thing to you. People in history were not a different race from you and me. Your history books deal mostly with the great people, the Kings and Princes and the Ministers of State. They're just the froth upon the surface; the Kings and Princes and the Ministers—they don't mean much. History is made by plain and simple people like ourselves, doing the best we can with each job as it comes along. Leif went out to get timber to build cowhouses, and found America. That's how real people make real history. You may make history yourselves one day, any one of you, but you may never know you've done it. Leif didn't. (*Pause*) All right, you can go now.

(*The* BOYS *get up and begin to stream out of the classroom. The* HEADMASTER *is standing in the passage looking very sour; as the* BOYS *pass him talking eagerly among themselves, his frown deepens.*)

BOY TWO I say, I liked the bit about Eric fighting with an axe. The groundsman's got an axe. I don't believe the tool shed is locked up.

BOY ONE I don't believe it's true, any of it. There's nothing about it in the book. It says John Cabot discovered North America.

BOY THREE He said the books were all wrong; they only tell you what the Kings and Princes did. I'm not going to bother with my history book any more. I'd rather listen to him talking.

BOY FOUR I liked the bit about Thorgunna. We've never had

125

a history master tell us the ripe bits before. I hope he keeps it up.

(*They pass, and* CALLENDER *follows them out of the room; he comes face to face with the* HEADMASTER. *They look at each other in silence for a moment.*)

CALLENDER (*Nervously*) Was that all right, sir?

HEADMASTER (*Reflectively*) Princes and Kings and Ministers are just the froth upon the surface. And all the books are wrong. And all these boys are going to make history. And Thorgunna had a baby. As a first lesson on the History of the United States, it was certainly original.

CALLENDER (*Diffidently*) As a matter of fact, I was coming on to that next time. I was going to tell them all about the Boston Tea Party. I think they'd like that.

HEADMASTER Very, very interesting. (*Looks at* CALLENDER) Didn't you say that you have a friend who offered you a job to sell electric razors in Paris?

CALLENDER Yes, sir.

HEADMASTER (*Thoughtfully*) Do you know, I think if I were you I should be rather inclined to take it.

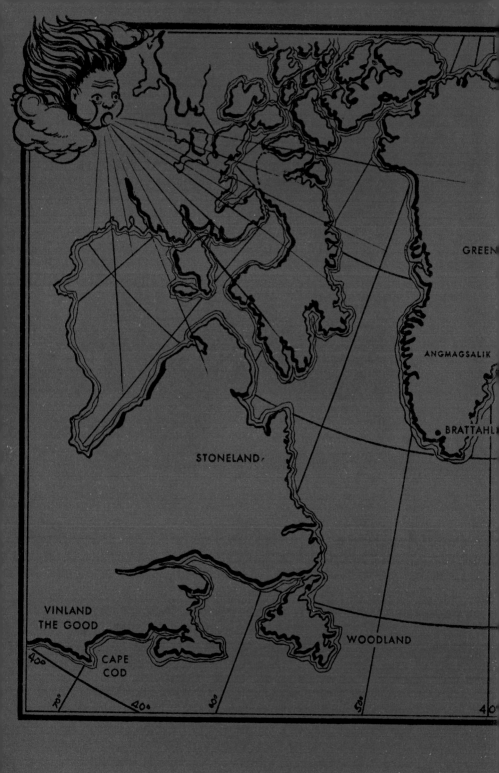

GREEN

ANGMAGSALIK

• BRATTAHLI

STONELAND

VINLAND
THE GOOD

CAPE
COD

WOODLAND

40°

70°

40°

30°

50°

40